The Gospel of

POLITICAL CORRECTNESS

By
Rev. Peter Mullen

Being the Life of Bossy of Islington

First Published 2012
Copyright © Rev. Peter Mullen 2012

Bretwalda Books
Unit 8, Fir Tree Close, Epsom, Surrey KT17 3LD
www.BretwaldaBooks.com

To receive an e-catalogue of our complete range of books
send an email to info@BretwaldaBooks.com

ISBN 978-1-909099-22-7

Bretwalda Books Ltd

"Beware of false prophets which come to you in sheep's clothing, but inwardly are ravening wolves"

Matthew ch.7 v.15

CONTENTS

 *The Prologue*

In which BOSSY of ISLINGTON tells the story of his BIRTH

his is the generation of him that is called Bossy of Islington, the Moderniser General: And, behold, I looked and saw that there is no generation set down, for the Politically Correct hath decreed that verily the boasting of genealogy is but a vain thin, sexist and elitist and belongeth rather to the old time which hath passed away.

And it came to pass in those days that went out a decree from the Prime Bureaucrat that the whole land should be overtaxed to pay the tribute to the False God ERM, that is surnamed Evercloserunion.

And all went to be overtaxed, everyone into his (or her) own city. And Wayne also went up from Essex, out of the city of Southend, unto London to be overtaxed with Rubella his partner, being up the duff. There they stayed in the garden shed of his grandad Dave for Dave was renting his bedrooms out to asylum seekers so there was no room in the house. And so it was that the days were accomplished that she would sprog.

And she brought forth her firstborn son, and wrapped him in a babygro from Lidl with a fetching fake aquacutum check design and laid him in that box the lager came in, for Wayne had pissed against the wall all the dosh she had saved for a pram.

And there were in the same country, estate agents abiding in the fields, keeping watch over land prices by night. And hearing a commotion they did go into the council estate and did hear a voice singing "Behold, I bring thee a brilliant news flash, which shall be to all People irrespective of race, creed, colour, sexual orientation or disability. For unto you is born this day outside the house of Dave a Moderniser General which is called Bossy, according to the promos and the long trailers for all this which thou hast no doubt seen on the telly. And this shall be a sign unto you, Ye shall find the sprog wrapped in a fake aquascutum babygro, lying in that cardboard box the lager came in."

And it came to pass that the estate agents said to one another, "Let us go now even unto the house of Dave

and see this thing which is come to pass, which the Latest Thing hath made known unto us." And they came with haste and found the shed in which was Rubella his mother, and Wayne and the sprog, lying in a lager crate.

And when they had seen him, they went abroad telling that people would live in a shed in London and speculating how much commission they could charge on selling sheds. And they also told the saying which was told them concerning this sprog. And all they that heard it were flipped out at these things that were spoken unto them by the estate agents.

But Rubella kept all these things up her jumper and said nowt to nobody.

Now, when the Moderniser General was born Bossy of Islington, in the Great City, in the days of the Prime Bureaucrat who was not Politically Correct, behold there came non-discriminatory persons of multi-cultural backgrounds from the East End unto the street that is called Downing, saying, "Where is he (or she) that is born to bring this country to be Politically Correct? For we read his (or her) horoscope in The Star and are come to check him (or her) out for compliance under the laws of health and safety."

When the Prime Bureaucrat who was not Politically Correct heard these things he was all, like, unglued, and all Downing Street with him. And when he had gathered all the physicians of that which is called "spin", he enquired of them privily where the Moderniser General should be born.

And they say unto him, in Islington of the Great City: for thus it is written by the focus group, "And thou Islington in the land of Equal Opportunities art not least among honchos of the People, for out of thee shall come a prophet that shall rule in all the land called Nanny State. And Britain will become the Land of Political Correctness."

Then the Prime Bureaucrat who was not Politically Correct sent then to Islington and saith "Please check it out, and when thou hast found the child, bring me an update that I may organise a photo-opportunity."

And when they were come unto the garage round the back of the tower block of the public housing unit - let him that readeth understand - they saw the kid with Rubella his mother, and fell down and took many snaps of them on their digital cameras: and when they had opened their *Gucci* bags they bought forth gifts of alchopops, DVDs and *viagra*.

And being warned of the approach of the *Daily Mail* astrologer, they departed into the East End by another way. They mounted the 25 bus, for lo, the Central Line was all screwed up as the custom is.

And when they were departed, behold, a vision appeareth to Wayne, rolling a joint, saying, "Arise and take the sprog and his mum and flee to Egypt."

And Wayne saith unto him, "Egypt - not bloody likely! There's all sand there and no human rights, and that!"

And, behold, the vision saith, "Well, get thee unto Neasden then. And be thou there until I bring thee word. For the Prime Bureaucrat who was not Politically Correct will seek the young sprog to ban him from the playgroup." When he arose, he took the young sprog and his mum by night and departed even unto Neasden.

The non-PC Prime Bureaucrat, when he saw that he was mocked by the non-discrimatory persons, was exceeding wroth, so that, as they say in their language, he went ballistic and banished all the young children in the Great City (from two years old and under) from playgroup.

Then was fulfilled that which was spoken by the Guru, saying, "In the Great City was there a voice heard, lamentation and weeping and great mourning. Single mothers doing their nut because the kids were barred from the playgroup and they couldn't get no childcare while they sought to go forth on the piss."

And when the non-PC Prime Bureaucrat was kicked out of Downing Street, behold, a vision appeareth unto Wayne, which was legless in Neasden, saying, "Sober up, man, and take the young sprog and his mum and go into the Great City, for they have lost the election which sought to ban the kid from the playgroup."

And he arose and took the young sprog and his mum and came even unto the Great City. But when Wayne heard that the new Prime Bureaucrat with the Toothy Grin did reign in that place, which cometh after the old non-PC Prime Bureaucrat that was gone to watch the cricket, he was afraid to go there. So he turned aside into the parts of Essex. And he came and dwelt in a town called Southend, that it might be fulfilled which was spoken by the Guru, "He shall be called a Sarfender."

At least this is the version told by Bossy of Islington.

Chapter One

In which BOSSY BEGINS to PREACH

nd it came to pass that the years rolled away. And the Prime Bureaucrat with the Toothy Grin was ousted in his turn and replaced by the Prime Bureaucrat who did Throw Phones who was ousted in his turn and replaced by the Prime Bureaucrat who did Agree with Nick who was ousted in his turn and replaced by the Prime Bureaucrat who Knew Not What He Did.

In those days cometh Jak the Aquatherapist, which did dip folk in the Serpentine, saying, "Change! Be positive and upbeat - for Cloud Cuckoo Land is at hand!"

And this same Jak had his raiment a camel-hair coat and a leather thong about his loins; and his wholefood diet was organic locusts and prime honey from selected hives. For he was once a man of great wealth, a banker in the Great City who had failed to hedge his funds appropriately against the financial crash and was now living in a cardboard box underneath the arches. Then went out to him all the Great City and all the People along the banks of the Thames. And, behold, he did minister unto them, "Go shopping - for the Latest Thing is at hand!" And they every one of them promised to chuck out all their old things and buy new things all the time.

But when he saw Fogey, he of the tweed jacket that did speak on ITV and Capital Radio, he crieth out, "O generation of has-beens! Who hath warned thee there be another promo on the way? Rend ye not your hearts but rend your garments and get ye to Harvey Nicks for some new gear. And think not to say we have plenty of nice pairs of flannels in the wardrobe and Harris tweed for our jackets, for I say unto to you that the Latest Thing is able of these very special offers to raise up a whole new Lifestyle. For we can spend our way out of the recession. And forget thy debt for are not interest rates low and if Greece does not pay its debts why should you?

"For I indeed do render you aquatherapy unto energising, but he that cometh after me is more cutting-edge that I, whose flip-flops I am not worthy to wash,

11

and he will give unto thee the complete detox. For his aquatherapy is mightier than mine and he will give thee total infusion with the Spirit of the Age and special Javanese chilli powder and shall make thee joyously Politically Correct."

Then cometh Bossy from Southend unto Jak to be aquatherapised by him. But Jak forbade him, saying, "I have need to be detoxed by thee; and do thou come unto me for aquatherapy?"

But Bossy, answering, saith, "Let it be for this promo, according to the script."

And Bossy, when he was aquatherapised, went up straightway out of the water and, behold, the adverts came on and the music played and the Spirit of the Age descended upon him like it was wont to do on *Children in Need Day*. And lo, a voice from the producer's office, saying, "This is the Latest Thing On Earth. He's gonna make it - bigtime."

And Bossy did talk with Jak the Aquatherapist about libor rates and interbank lending and sub prime mortgages and such high financial sayings. And Jak the Aquatherapist did tell Bossy about Dom Perignon and Ferrari and Versaci and other rewards of the rich. And Bossy did listen.

Then did Jak the Aquatherapist speak after this fashion. "Listen, kid. The West is rich and prosperous, but many of the richest and most prosperous are wracked by guilt. They went to posh private schools and have done well for themselves, and they liketh the champers and the Armani and the fast cars, but they look on the poor of the third world and feel guilty. Behold they desireth to assuage that guilt, but without giving up the champers and the Armani and the fast cars.

"And so I offer aquatherapy that they might cleanse themselves of guilt. And in so doing I cleanse myself of my guilt for having had my snout in the trough of the bankers bonuses."

13

And Bossy did question Jak the Aquatherapist in this wise, saying "So by undergoing your aquatherapy these people join the ranks of the righteous."

"Verily so," saith Jak. "And they can then feel smug and superior for they are enlightened and they can pour scorn on those who have the champers and the Armani and the fast cars, but doeth not the aquatherapy. Likewise can they pour scorn on those who are poor or are chavs or are otherwise not fit to sit at their tables. Even more smug are they that hold the true beliefs of the righteous. They that promote multiculturalism can smugly scorn others as racists, they that buy carbon credits can proclaim they save the earth and so be even more content and with it, they that send their children to a comprehensive that lieth in a posh part of town where houses in the catchment area cost a damn fortune can thus heap abuse on those who live in poor council estates but work hard to get their kids a good education. Thus do the righteous enjoy their privileges, while feeling smug about their goodness."

Then did Bossy ask "So what's in for you, then?"

"I gain my redemption for my past sins by doing good unto others," quoth Jak the Aquatherapist.

"Daft old bugger," saith Bossy, "taketh thou not their cash? They've got loads, lets face it."

"Virtue is its own reward," saith Jak. And he did write that on a placard and proclaim the words along the banks of the Serpentine. Whereupon Jak was taken away by the police for holding a demonstration without permission. And lo the magistrate sent him unto the care-in-the-community home.

Then was Bossy walking the streets of London while he thought on the words of Jak the Aquatherapist. And he knocked around forty nights and slept for forty days, he was afterwards, like, peckish. And he was sitting on a bench in the churchyard of St Anne's, even that which opens on to Wardour Street in Soho, when Sebastian the Agent came to him. Sebastian was lamenting saying "All my actors are gone to make adverts in Peckham and I no longer have a talent to represent." He looketh at

Bossy and said, "If thou be the Guy with the Latest Thing, command that these empty fag packets be made *ciabatta*."

But Bossy answereth and saith, "It is written, thou shalt not live by ciabatta alone, but by going up into *The Ivy* and even unto *Le Caprice* and partaking of the posh scoff that therein is." And Sebastian the Agent was impressed.

Then Sebastian the Agent taketh Bossy into the City and setteth him by a window up the Gherkin, and saith unto him, "If thou be the Guy with the Latest Thing, chuck thyself. For verily I shall video thee on the way down and, behold, it looketh fab on the snuff movies."

And Bossy saith unto him, "But verily that is not a trick thou canst do twice and I seek a longer career that will see us both as rich as Midas." And Sebastian the Agent was mightily impressed. And they did speak about the guilt felt by the rich, who wished to assuage that guilt by raising taxes that everyone else had to pay, and who would want to feel smug by being part of the in group of the Politically Correct, such that they could be kind and tolerant while keeping hold of their wealth. And could laugh to scorn and persecute those that were not Politically Correct. And Sebastian and Bossy did discover the way to righteousness and to riches.

Again, Sebastian the Agent taketh Bossy up an exceeding high tower block and sheweth him all the theatre and cinemas, pubs, clubs and revue bars of the West End and saith unto him, "Lo, I can make thee a star in all these joints if thou wilt pay unto me a commission of twenty-five per cent."

And Bossy saith, "Look sonny, I'm the Latest Thing on Earth and I'm going solo. Sod thou off!"

Then Sebastian the Agent agreed that ten per cent was reasonable and went off to open a special bank account in the name of an offshore corporation based in the Bahamas. And, behold, he shivered for he feeleth the force of the Vibes in that place.

And Bossy came and dwelt in Shepherd's Bush, which is towards the West and handy for the Beeb, that it might be fulfilled which was spoken by the Guru, saying, "The People that sat in darkness in front of the telly have seen a great new series; and they that could foretime receive only ITV have now got digital."

From that time Bossy began his stand-up act and to say, "Wotcha cock - I'm the Latest Thing on Earth!" But Bossy knew that the work he had to do was great and would need groupies.

And Bossy, coming into the northern parts and walking by Camden Lock saw two guys, Simmy which was called Pete due to his being on the run from an asbo, and Andy, his mate, playing the one-armed bandits in the arcade, for verily they were the kids on the block. And straightway they left the bandits and followed him.

And going on from thence he seeth two other mates, Jim the son of Zeb, and Jon, his stepbrother by the new partner of his mother, with the which she was in an ongoing relationship. And they all immediately left their slot machines and became his groupies. And so did Randy Phil who reckoned all the best crumpet were right-on trendy lefties. And also Bart, who felt that the BNP had gone soft and fancied a bit of a change.

And Bossy went about all their community centres promoting equal opportunities, non-discrimination and social inclusion, and did preach the gospel of Political-Correctness and healed all manner of psychoneurosis among the malingerers. And his fame spread throughout all the City and they bring unto him all them that were taken with divers fashionable complaints, even with ME, post-traumatic stress disorder and Munchausen Syndrome by Proxy. And there followed him a great multitude of hangers-on and prurient sentimentalists from the City, from Shepherd's Bush and from all the region round about Essex.

And Sebastian the Agent was no damn fool, so he went to the Beeb to tell them of a powerful new working class prophet that was the Latest Thing. And the Beeb sent him a TV news crew to film the fashionable new lefty phenomenon.

And seeing the whole multitude of the great unwashed, Bossy went up on to the Hill that is called Primrose, and when he was set his groupies came unto him. And he waited until he saw Sesbastian and the Beeb TV crew. Then he opened his mouth and gave them a presentation, saying, "The Truth is greater than the facts. Any damn fool with an internet connection can tell thee the facts, but only I can tell thee the Truth.

"Chipper are the poor Millwall supporters, for they have been drawn against Arsenal and Wiltshire has sprained his ankle.

"Chirpy are they that mourn, for they shall receive bereavement counselling.

"Ecstatic are the bashful, for they shall get assertiveness training.

"Buggered are they that do hunger and thirst after righteousness, for there's not much of that around these days.

"Right chuffed are the sentimental, for it's Princess Di Day next week.

"In luck are the impure of heart, 'cos there's lots of stuff for them on video and late-nite telly.

"Perky are they that belong to the peacekeeping process, for they shall revise the compliance manual.

"Happy are ye, when Fogey and old farts shall revile you and say all manner of racist and sexist things against you. Great is thy reward in Cloud Cuckoo land, for so persecuted they the Gurus that were before you.

"Ye are the salt of the crisp packet, but if the salt produceth raised blood pressure then verily thou shalt take statins.

"Think not that I am come to destroy Standard Practice. I am come not to destroy but to fulfil. For verily I say unto you, Till Cloud Cuckoo Land and Medialand pass away, one jot or tittle shall in no wise pass from Standard Practice, till all be compliance.

"Whosever therefore shall break one of these least footling proscriptions and shall teach his neighbour to say, 'Bollocks to Political-Correctness' shall be called the least in the Nanny State, and whosoever shall do and teach total compliance shall be greatest in the Nanny State.

"Ye have heard it was said of them in the old time, 'Thou shalt not kill. And whosoever shall kill shall be in danger of being strung up.' But I say unto you, whosoever shall kill shall be henceforth called a 'Victim' and 'Vulnerable' and shall receive psychotheraphy. Verily I say unto that his deed shall be set at nought. And the matter shall not be allowed to drop until all the psychiatric reports have been accepted.

"And whosoever shall say unto his colleague, 'Thou nerd or *schemiel* or pointy-head' shall be in danger of being monitored; but whoso calleth his colleague 'proper jerk' shall be in danger of social exclusion.

"Therefore if thou bring thy floral tribute to the roadside shrine at the end of thy neighbour's drive and there rememberest that thy colleague hath aught against thee, leave thy floral tribute by the roadside shrine, sign thee up for one of the conciliation courses according as the Compatibility Restoration Counsellor commandeth thee, then come and offer thy floral tribute at the roadside shrine which is at the end of the drive of thy neighbour.

"Seek compliance with him that is suing thee quickly while thou art on thy mobile to him, lest at any time he that is suing thee report thee to the Internal Examiner and the Internal Examiner deliver thee to the Psychotherapist and the Psychotherapist to the funny farm. Verily thou shalt in no wise come out thence until all the psychiatric casework hath been fulfilled.

"Ye have heard that it was said by them of old time, 'Thou shalt not commit adultery, nor shalt they covet thy neighbour's wife nor they neighbour's ass', but I say unto you, 'Commit adultery as often as thou canst get thine end away, mate, for it is a liberated thing to put it around a bit, like. Only thou shalt wear a condom.'

"It hath been said, 'Whosoever shall put away his wife, let him give her a bill of divorcement.' But I say unto you that divorces, yea and even marriages, are but a small thing and to be taken up or set down as the whim taketh thee. It is good for men and women to enjoy many partners and verily to eschew all that monogamy and chauvinistic crap which were afore Modern Times.

"Again it hath been said, thou shalt not forswear thyself nor take the name of the Latest Thing in vain. But I say unto thee, that which was formerly abominable hath passed away, and now, as the custom is, they swear every other word on the telly. Be fruitful and expostulate as you wish.

"Ye have heard that it hath been said, 'An eye for an eye and a tooth for a tooth.' But I say unto you punishment is a very negative thing and a part of the whole blame culture. Therefore, rather say I unto thee that, when offences come, thou shalt turn a blind eye. But whosoever smite thee on thy right cheek, thou mayest sue him in the small claims court for invading thy personal space.

"And whoso shall compel thee to go a kilometre, jog with him two; for thus shall thy calories fall away and thy cholesterol be lowered. And the last state of man is better than the first.

"But if a man ask thee for thy cloak, tell him to get stuffed and go shopping for his own designer clobber at the *Nicks* which is called *Harvey* according as the Latest Thing hath commanded."

After saying these things, he departed from the region about the Hill that is Primrose and entered again into Essex. And Sebastian sent him a text saying "Great work. The mugs are falling for it big time. Get ready for prime time.   :o)"

Chapter Two

In which BOSSY cures the SICK and the THICK

nd Bossy cometh into the house of Sim (which is called Pete) and Sim's mother lay sick with a fever. And Sim saith unto Bossy, "Verily she is a right on for crogging it on and believeth now that she hath the 'flu which is called bird'."

And he went in unto the back bedroom wherein she sniffeth and wheezeth and he saith unto Sim, "She sulketh for thou makest the more fuss over me, thy new friend, than thou wast wont to make over her. Behold, it is called in the language of the physicians Attention-Seeking Syndrome, a disease psychosomatic." And he took her by the hand and said unto her, "Woman, arise and be not grievously vexed with the Attention-Seeking Syndrome. I say unto thee, sulk thou not and even lighten up!"

And straightaway the Attention-Seeking Syndrome left her and she did lighten up and maketh them all a cup of tea. And the People marvelled.

And at even, when the sun did set, there came unto him all the nutters and hysterics and malingerers, and his groupies said, "Tell them to sod off for, behold, they suffer from that which is called Personality Disorder."

But Bossy produced a stack of business cards, and handing one to each of the nutters he saith, "Go show thyself unto the counsellor that counselleth for the Personality Disorder according as the Standard Practice commandeth thee. And make sure that thou hast a valid credit card to pay the bill. And if thou hast not a valid credit card thou must fill in the form from the Social so that they pay instead."

And they did all go, and behold, they were every one of them lightened up and were no more vexed by the Personality Disorder. And next day did Sebastian go to the counsellors to get the referral fee agreed in advance, the same that was paid into the special bank account.

Again Bossy entered into the house and they bring one unto him that lieth on a bed, sick of hangover, and they beseech him that he might heal him. Bossy turneth to him that was sick of the hangover and saith, "Cheer up old son! Take thou the very hair of the dog."

But there was there a man called Fogey, he with the chat show on ITV, who objected saying "Behold, Bossy goeth against Standard Practice for he commandeth this man to cheer up and have another drink. Yet giving a drunk a drink makes him an alocohoic. And a hangover is self-imposed and the man must suffer so that he does not again get drunk when he should be at work."

And others who there all with one accord began to murmur against Bossy and would feign have duffed him up. But he, percieving that which was in their hearts, saith, "Why reason ye these things in your hearts and why do ye say these things against me? For whether it is easier to say 'Cheer up!' or 'Arise, take up thy bed, get thee to the boozer and start getting pissed again'? But, that ye may know that the Son of Wayne hath power on earth to tell men to lighten up." He turned to the crashed-out alcy and saith,

"Shift thyself matey, and see thou gettest out a bit more!"

And he that was the crashed-out alcy arose, took up his bed and belteth off downtown at a rate of knots, and lo, he cheereth up exceedingly and shaketh it all about as Bossy had commanded him.

And the people all marvelled, saying, "What manner of a man is this that he telleth the attention-seekers to snap out of it and he that sulketh to cheer up, and even the miserable old gits obey him?"

And so he did sit down and eat with his groupies. And there came unto him all the disadvantaged and underprivileged of the inner city for to eat with him.

Now Fogey said unto the groupies, "How is it that he eateth with the disadvantaged and underprivileged and them that are socially-excluded and from the shitty end of town?"

When Bossy heard it he was wroth and saith, "It is not the compliant which have need of the Standards Inspection Officer but they which are in breech of sections or subsections of the Manual of Procedure. And those that are intelligent will understand and those that are thick will continue to ask damn fool questions."

And no man any longer durst ask him say more damn fool questions for no man wanted to appear to be thick in front of his mates.

And it came to pass that, as he walked with his groupies through Colchester on one of the Diana Days, and did eat some of the special choccies that he took from a roadside shrine to a car crash victim. And Fogey said unto him, "Behold, why dost thou and thy groupies eat of the choccies which are appointed but for the Shrine to be set there for the Festival which is called 'Lachrymae'?"

But Bossy saith unto them, "Have ye not heard what Dave did when he was peckish and fancied a bit of choccie - how he took the sacred Organic Mars Bar, and they that were with him, and did scoff until they damn near puketh?"

And Fogey could not answer to him again to any of these things from out of their mouths. And Fogey went his way.

In those days he passed through all the land of Essex and the country round about, teaching the gospel of Political-Correctness and delivering the People from all manner of imaginary diseases.

And when he drew nigh unto the Community Centre in the place that is called Basildon, a distraught father brought unto him one that was much lacking in the department which is called, in their language, gumption and as it saith in the Greek vous.

Simmy the Groupie said unto him, "This one is verily as thick as two short planks."

And Bossy answered them and said, "Sayest thou not that he is as thick as two short planks, but that he hath learning difficulties. For lo, he is but two sandwiches short of the feeding of the five thousand."

And they say unto him, "But master, he watcheth old Val Doonican videos and collecteth Embassy cigarette cards which were aforetime but are no more. Besides these things, behold, he singeth Shirley Bassey songs and offendeth against his neighbour. Surely he is as thick as two short planks!"

Bossy turneth unto him that hath the learning difficulties and saith, "What sayest thou concerning thy learning difficulties, for verily they that accuse thee declare thou art as thick as two short planks? Dost thou know what thou sayest?"

And he crieth with a loud voice,

"Now Patrick McGinty, an Irishman of note
Fell in for a fortune and he bought himself a goat..."

And, behold, the Basildon locals picked up stones wherewith to stone him. Yet holdeth he not his tongue, but cried out all the more in the manner of the Doonican that is called Val,

"Says he, sure of goat's milk I'm goin' home to have me fill

But when he brought a Nanny home, he found it was a Bill..."

And Bossy put his fingers over the man's mouth and saith, "Peace! Be still! And cry no more of the Doonican that is called Val, neither of that Paddy McGinty; and let not the gender of the goats be so much as mentioned among you. But be thou delivered of thy learning difficulties and be no more plankish. And instead go and learn something useful for a politically correct career."

And straightway he held his tongue and arose and took himself to the Enrolling Officer and the Enrolling Officer enrolled him in the Southend University, and he taketh his degree in Media Studies with Golf and Ten-Pin Bowling.

And the People marvelled, saying, "He hath done things well. He maketh him that hath the learning difficulties to have no more the learning difficulties; and behold, the two short planks are not short with him."

And Sebastian the Agent sent an email round the Vice Chancellors of all the universities in the land asking them what referral fees they would pay for new students who would sign up to really cheap courses that yet attracted valuable government subsidies. And he read the replies and grew wonderfully smug. And he sendeth a text to Bossy that read "Behold the credit card is in the post, but taketh care not to blow the lot. And lo! The website is up and running. Access codes to follow."

Chapter Three

In which BOSSY
announces the
establishment of
THE NEW CHURCH

nd when his groupies had gathered round, Bossy spake unto them in his doctrine and said, "When thou givest thine alms be certain that thou makest a song and dance about it, even a huge ballyhoo. Ye have heard it said, 'Do thy goodness by stealth and let no man see what thou doest.'

"But I say unto you, when thou doest aught for charity, shout it from the housetops. And if it so be that it is *Red Nose Day*, the put on thy red nose. And if it be *Children in Need*, then take thee to the humourless abasements and feign to have a good time. And on *World AIDS Day*, wear thy condom openly, that all may see it and rejoice that thou expressest solidarity with them that have fallen sick from their too much batting for the other side, and that which is called in their language 'the rear-entry method'. She that hath ears to hear, let her hear.

Then Andy the Groupie said unto him, "Oh Bossy, teach us of the Latest Thing and how we might draw nigh unto the Latest Thing so that we might be really with it and totally politically correct so that we can pull those right on chicks."

He saith unto them, "Thou shall love the Latest Thing with all thy heart, with all thy soul and with all thy strength, and thyself before thy neighbour."

But Andy the Groupie spake again saying "My father is one of the old farts who goeth to Church on Sunday. Therein lies a bastion of the non-Politically Correct Brigade. I am afeared to go unto this Church, but my father demandeth it of me."

Bossy replied. "Goeth thee with the old farts, for those who are not with us are against us and those who are not against us are with us. And behave in this wise. When ye pray, take thee to the midst of the assembly, jig about a bit, like; and wave thine arms so that they say, 'Behold, he hath learning difficulties'; and even the old farts and the politically-incorrect do say, 'Verily he's a frigging loony!'

"And in that which is called among them 'The Peace',

do thou fawn on thy neighbour and make abundant greeting and kiss him or her with great zeal, so that the old farts do ask, 'Is he trying to score with that bird, or what?'

"And when thou prayest be not as the old farts are, which make vain repetitions from books which are old and make those petitions which were spoken of them in the old time. For they do say, 'O lords, the only ruler of princes...' and other such things which be an abomination to the Latest Thing. Verily I say unto thee, they have their reward.

"But when thou prayest, let thy praying be from the book that is modernised and which payeth not regard for those things that are discriminatory on grounds of gender, race and class. Let thy petitions be for them that are called underprivileged, disadvantaged and vulnerable - and whatsoever the new buzz phrase is for them that are flavour of the month, do thou pray for them, as it happeneth asylum seekers or them that are transgendered or the insurgent which doth insurge against thy People in a strange land.

"And afterward take thee for Fair Trade coffee and devour thee plentifully of the biscuits that are from dodgy countries and that taste even very dodgy. Remember, when thou prayest, that thou use the guitar abundantly. And seek out for her that prayesth the fat woman with the voice that be exceedingly sanctimonious and she that doth cover her face with all manner of adornment so that the People say, 'Blimey, someone's given her a right paint job!'

"And when thou prayest, behold, make thee long prayers, even prayers that are very long; and endeth not when the old farts shall say, 'Bloody hell, she goeth on a bit!' Neither when they that are of the old farts party say, 'Fancy coming to church in a skirt like that! Behold, thou couldst see her very bum.'

"And do thou make sure thou hast switched on the microphones, that thou mayest be heard of women and men to pray. And when thy prayer is heard among women and men, thou shalt receive a round of applause according to the Latest Thing.

"After this manner therefore pray,
'O Latest Thing
Which art to die for,
Funky be thy name.
Thy newness come,
Thy cutting edge done
In our Lifestyle
As it is on the telly.
Give us this day our daily fix
And forgive us our political-incorrectness
But we don't forgive them that are political-incorrect against us.
Lead us into temptation

And deliver us from boredom,
For thine is the attitude,
The modernisation and the entertainment
Twenty-four seven
A-person.'"

But Andy the Groupie said "Master, the old farts will crucify me for sure."

Bossy smiled saying "All things will come to pass. We have bretheren among the heirarchy of the old farts who do our bidding. They believe not the virgin birth and the truth of the resurrection and all that mumbo jumbo. They believe in our trendy stuff and that which is PC and that which is pinko-liberal. They turn the Church to the side of the underprivileged - like that Occupy mob who went to private schools and posh universities but spake PC on behalf of the chavs. Verily I say unto thee. The Church shall turn against the old farts. So go thee with they father and do as I have said, and ye shall be the Latest Thing in the eyes of the bishop."

And Jim the son of Zeb asked this wise. "Master I go

not unto church with the old farts on a Sunday as I always have a hangover. And oft times the bird I pulled is also with hangover and wants not to go to church. Wherefore should I behave?"

And Bossy replied "When thou goest forth on the binge, adorn thyself in thy best clobber and anoint thyself with the unguents, perfumes and costly lotions that thou seest advertised in the supplements which are coloured, that they which see thee binge may know for a surety that thou art on the binge. And, behold, divers of these lotions do attract the birds like there's no tomorrow, like; even as it is said of them, 'they panteth for it'.

"Thou shalt not anoint thyself with the balm that is called in their language *Old Spice*, the balm that is used of the old farts. Verily they have their reward.

"Lay up treasure for thyself in equities and bonds where neither moth nor rust doth corrupt and where thieves do not break through and steal. For where thy treasure is, there shall thy Lifestyle be also.

"And see that thou dost indeed serve two masters, for when thou pleasest the one thou shalt please the other also. Thou canst easily serve the Latest Thing and Lifestyle.

"Take thee thought for thy life, what thou shalt eat and what thou shalt drink, and the designer clobber that thou shalt put on. For is not Lifestyle altogether that thou consumest? And, behold, the tills they rattle throughout the shopping precincts.

"Consider Lily, who hath that nice little boutique by St Martin-in-the-Fields, and even the birds of the catwalk, for they take thought by day and by night what they shall put on, and verily the Latest Thing becometh them. And lo, the Solomon Grundies in all their fogeyness are not arrayed like *Roberto Cavalli*.

"Wherefore if the Latest Thing so clothe the underprivileged and disadvantaged and even the Chavs from the inner city with pirated designer labels from off the peg, how much niftier shalt thou be clothed, O ye loadsamoney?

"And take thee thought of the morrow, where thou shalt binge and whom thou shalt screw. 'Cos it's important to have these things worked out aforehand, like.

"Judge and thou shalt be judged, for hath not the Latest Thing decreed that behold, Lifestyle is a beauty contest?

"And why beholdest thou the mascara that doth adorn thy sister's eye? Thou airhead! First use thine own proprietary cleansing cream as it commandeth thee in the supplements, then thou shalt see clearly to remove the mascara that is thy sister's.

"Give not that which is new and cool to the dogs which do hang about the disco, neither cast thou thy pearls before the swine that would tear them form thy neck on thy way back from the Ladies.

"Ask, and it shall be given thee - if thou nag and pester long enough. Seek and thou shalt find. And if thou seekest and findest not, then, behold, thou shalt chuck it and buy another one.

"Therefore, whosoever hearkeneth unto these promos of mine and the fashion statements that I have spoken unto thee, he is like one who purchased a house in Islington and, behold, when the property prices went through the roof, he maketh a killing and saith, 'I'm all right, mate. I bought at the right time!' And he moveth even unto Chelsea.

"But to him that getteth him a house in Chelsea when prices are at an all-time high, then I say unto him, 'Thou fool!' And the last state of that man is worse than the first."

Chapter Four

In which BOSSY doth put the FRIGHTENERS on the ANIMAL RIGHTS FANATICS

nd the third day there was a celebration of a civil partnership in Soho and Bossy's old lady was there. And both Bossy was called and his groupies to the piss-up.

And when they wanted some more of that strong cider, the old lady of Bossy saith unto him, "They've none of that strong cider."

Bossy saith unto her, "Old lady, why givest thou grief? S'not as if it's my fault is it? I'm only here for that thou demandest of me that I come to the piss-up of the civil partnership of thy friends Jeremy and Jamie."

His old lady saith unto the caterers, "Whatsoever he saith unto you, do it."

And there were set there six canisters of plastic after the manner of the non-drinking of the *Alcoholics Anonymous*, containing thirty or forty pints of water apiece. And Bossy saith unto them caterers, "Carry those canisters of water and come with me."

And they carried them to a dingy doorway in Old Compton Street and Bossy saith "Put the canisters here, then pop to the Admiral Duncan for a quick half and come back in ten minutes. And the caterers departed while Bossy did speak unto the woman in the dingy doorway. Then the caterers returned and carried the canisters back unto the party, and Bossy saith unto them, "Draw out now and bear unto the guvnor." And they bear it.

When the guvnor of the piss-up had tasted of the strong cider that was drawn from the water canisters, and knew not whence it was, but the flunkeys which drew the water knew, the guvnor of the piss-up calleth one of the Gay couple and saith unto him,

"Every guy at the beginning doth set forth great booze, and when everyone falleth about pissed, like, then cometh the crappy two per cent by volume rubbish which don't do nuffin' for nobody, like. But thou hast saved the lulu juice until now!"

"Whazup" spake the groom, for he was mightily far gone on the booze. "Izzz alrigh. I gone got the organic zider stuff, din I?" And he looketh at Bossy.

"Verily," quoth Bossy. "It is cider of the organic kind. And all is well if one but drink the organic booze."

This beginning of promos did Bossy in Soho of the Great City, and manifested forth his coolness. And his groupies thought he was the Latest Thing.

And, behold, they went from thence unto the country of them that speak in the language of Estuary which is over against Essex towards the forest. And there met him out of the town a certain guy which was grievously tormented. He wore not clothes, neither abode in any house but ran about the municipal cemetery.

And one of his groupies, called Bart, began to ask him, saying, "What's up with him then? He looks bloody crackers to me."

And Bossy was much displeased and answereth them, saying, "Say not that he is bloody crackers. Say rather that he hath the bipolar disorder which in the time of their political-incorrectness they were wont to call the manic-depressive psychosis."

And when he that hath the bipolar disorder seeth Bossy he cried out with a loud voice and fell down before him, saying, "Keep thine hands off me, thou Bossy, son of the Latest Thing. Don't come near me with thy therapy and thy counseling!"

(For Bossy had commanded the bipolar disorder to come out of the man. For oftentimes it had caught him so that he was tagged by order of the Bureaucrat. And he chucketh away the tagging wherewith he was tagged and was driven of the bipolar disorder into the cemetery.)

And Bossy asked him, "What is thy name?"

And he answereth, "Legion, for we are many."

And Bart turned unto Bossy and saith, "Sodding hell! It soundeth more like schizophrenia than bipolar disease to me."

And Bossy saith, "Thou hast spoken well, Bart. We'll make a doctor of thee yet - just like thine uncle Luke."

So he calleth the multitudinous schizophrenic abnormal personality manifestations diver longs names in the Latin tongue. And one of them cried in a loud

voice, "See that thou chuckest us not into the lake, we beseech thee! For we swim not."

And Bart saith unto Bossy, "See - I told thee he wast bloody crackers!" And, behold, he smirketh.

But Bossy turneth unto him and saith, "Smirk thou not. But that thou may know that the Latest Thing on Earth hath power to apply the correct therapy to both the bipolar disease and to the schizophrenia." He turneth to the loony and crieth, "Get thee into yonder load of pigs!"

And the loony was wroth and saith, "What meanest thou, get thee into the pigs, Guv? I might be a sodding loony but verily I'm no pig-shagger!"

Nevertheless he saith, "Again I say unto thee, Get thee into the pigs!"

Then went the bipolar disorder - or as it might be the multitudinous schizophrenic abnormal personality manifestations or even the bloody crackers - out of the man and into the pigs which ran violently down a deep place into the Estuary of the Thames and were drowned.

When they that fed the pigs, and whose the pigs were saw what was done, they spake unto Bossy and his groupies with many words, so that verily the air waxed blue. And they called RSPCA Inspection Officers. And the RSPCA Inspection Officers called the Animal Rights fanatics and the groupies were sore afraid.

But Bossy saith unto his groupies, "Be ye not affrighted, for behold, if I hear another peep out of these Animal Rights fanatic, I'll chuck them into the lake after the pigs. And then I will declare that they were non-PC and shall speak in the Press about how they stood up for the capitalist pig farmers against the interests of the poor schizophrenic - and lo the hate emails will come to afflict them. Thus it is written, or will be as soon as I post up their email addresses on our website."

Then a great fear came upon the Animal Rights fanatics and them that were of the RSPCA Inspection Office and they scarpereth. And the groupies did laugh them to scorn and Pete putteth forth his tongue and saith, "Ner-ner, Ne-ne-ner-ner-ner! That's got you bastards, annit?"

But afterward, Bart taketh Bossy apart and saith unto him, "Why doest thou, then? Why sendest thou the pigs into the estuary so that they are altogether perished out of the land? For we thought that thou wast he that wast in all things Politically-Correct, and that thou comest out to teach men the gospel of Political-Correctness."

And Bossy saith unto him, "Oh I dunno, Bart. Sometimes you just think you've gotta go for it!"

And they all begin to say with one voice, "Ah, Bossy, thou art a Right One!" And they call him "a proper card" and other such things as men say when they know in their hearts that this is the Gaffer.

And they departed out of the jurisdiction of the RSPCA Inspectors. And a great fear came upon all the Animal Rights fanatics and they say, "We had thought Bossy should be the one to teach us Political-Correctness in all things, but lo, he hath killed the pigs."

Others said, "Fret not, for it is his custom to teach the Political-Correctness. Behold, he wast stressed out and throweth a wobbly."

And they all with one accord call after him and say, "O Facilitator, do thou throw no more the wobbly and return ye not to our coasts!"

Then came to him his mother and his brethren, for of a truth he hath brethren by this time, for Wayne keepeth not his hands off Rubella so that it was said of her by her neighbours, "Behold, she's always up the duff, that one. Like unto rabbits they are, 'er and that Wayne." And they say again, "Like unto rabbits!"

And, behold, his mother and brethren could not get near him for the *paparazzi*. And it was told him by certain of the *paparazzi* which said, "Thy mother and thy brethren stand without, desiring to see thee."

And he saith unto them, "Without what?"

And they say, "Without a clue. Well, you know what they're like - behold, they are, like, six firkins short of a miraculous piss-up."

And he saith, "Who is my mother? Who are my

brethren? Verily I say unto you, that they that loveth the Latest Thing - they are my mother and my brethren."

Now it came to pass on the following Wednesday that he went into a ship with his groupies, for he saith unto them, "Behold, I am desirous of checking the water for sodium content and even for nitrates that it can be pure enough for the hypochondriacs of the PC persuasion that is called Green or Organic to drink."

And they launched forth. But as they sailed, he fell asleep and there came down a storm of wind over the Thames estuary and the ship was filled with water. And they were sore afraid, even so sore that they shit themselves. And that maketh them the more sore.

And they come to him and say, "Facilitator, Facilitator, we perish and lo, yet afore we perish we do shit ourselves!"

But he arose from sleep and saith, "Shit not yourselves for this verily is the manner of the tempest that ye should look for in days of the Global Warming. As it was foretold by the Green Guru where he saith:

"'Behold, the days come, when the cattle shall fart exceedingly and the chimneys shall smoke and the air shall be filled with greenhouse gases. And there shall be wailing and gnashing of teeth. And lo, it pisseth down a whole lot more that it was accustomed in the old times.'"

And he rebuketh the Global Warming and of a sudden there was great calm. And his groupies wondered and began to say among themselves, "Who is this that even the greenhouse gases do obey him?"

Chapter Five

In which BOSSY rebuketh HACK of the REDTOP RAG

nd when he was come down from the mountain, great multitudes followed him. And, behold, there came a man grievously vexed with *acne vulgaris*, which is called in their language pimples. And he worshipped him, saying, "Facilitator, if thou wilt thou canst make me clean of the pimples which are called pimples."

And Bossy had compassion upon the man that had the *acne vulgaris* for he perceiveth that it put the birds off no end. And he saith, "God, you look a proper sight!"

And he put forth his hand and touched him, saying, "Yuk, it's all, like, lumpy and that, innit? I can't do nothing about it, but get thee the health and beauty supplement and do buy for thyself the incredibly costly face cream advertised therein. And get thee to the disfigurement counsellor - here is his card, remember to mention my name - and offer thy

first instalment in the easy-pay therapy course for the aesthetically challenged."

And immediately the pimply man went forth unto the paper shop. And his groupies marvelled, seeing that such power was given unto men that he was able to send pock-marked pillocks to the newsagents.

And when Bossy was entered into Islington, behold, there came unto him a peace activist beseeching him, saying, "My servant lieth at home, differently-abled, grievously tormented."

But when he heard this saying, Bossy was wroth and rent his garment and saith unto the peace activist, "What is this that thou sayest, 'my servant'? Hast thou not heard of the Equal Opportunities Commission and the law which saith thou shalt not discriminate on the grounds of race, creed or class? How is it that thou hast a servant?"

And he could not answer him to any of these things.

And Bossy waxed exceeding wroth and saith unto him that hath the servant, "Come on now - thou hast a tongue in thine head. Answer thou me and keep not silence."

And he saith, "Facilitator, thou hast well spoken. Let him be no more my servant but my friend." And he fell at his feet and wept.

When he saw the things which had come to pass, Pete saith, "Look at that will you, boys - another freaking sentimentalist!"

And the peace activist denieth not, but confessed and said, "Facilitator, I am not worthy that thou shouldst come into my Pacifist Campaign HQ, but speak the word only and my servant - sorry, he that aforetime was my servant but that is verily now my friend - shall be healed."

The groupies begin to say, "Just hearken at him crogging it on. Talk about flannel!"

And the peace activist holdeth not his tongue, but confesseth openly, "For I am a man under authority, having peaceniks, CND members and other useful idiots under me. And I say to this person 'Go' and she goeth; and to another, 'Come' and she cometh; and to my servant - sorry, to the one that was aforetime my servant - 'Do this' and he doeth it."

And the Moderniser General turneth to his groupies and saith, "Hearken at all that! And I thought it was I that was called Bossy!"

And his groupies laughed so that they piss themselves.

And Bossy saith unto him that besought him, "Just have another go at framing thy request, sonny, and I'll see what I can do."

And when he had come to his right mind he beginneth again to ask for him that was aforetime his servant but was now called his friend, "For I am a man of equal opportunities and non-elitist, I beseech thee to heal him that is differently-abled."

And Bossy saith, "Ah, but not sick of the palsy, is he? Tell you what, mate, we're all bloody sick of the palsy!

What man among you isn't sick of the palsy?" And, behold, his groupies do wet themselves the second time.

And Bossy turneth to him that besought him and saith, "Go thy way. As thou hast spoken so shall it be done unto thee. Though I have not heard such bullshit - no, not in all Islington and Camden."

When the even was come they brought unto him many that were possessed with learning difficulties, and behold, he did cast out the learning difficulties and did write sick notes for all them that were desirous to be signed off on the sick, even them which suffered that which in the Latin tongue is called *oscillatio plumbi*.

Now when they see great multitudes coming upon them, the groupies gave commandment in his name, saying, "Piss ye off to the other side!"

And they all every one of them pissed off, saying, "He hath done all things well. He both signeth the sick notes for the malingerers and casteth out the learning difficulties. And, behold, he saith to this man, 'Piss off!' and straightaway he pisseth off."

And a certain Hack from *The Redtop Rag* cometh unto him and saith, "Facilitator, I will be thy groupie and follow thee whithersoever thou goest and write about thy doings in the supplement that is called Naff." And he produced his camera with the long lens and began taking photos.

And Bossy saith unto him, "So? I've got plenty of groupies already. Lo, the foxes have a hunting ban and the birds of the air are protected by the commissars in the RSPB; but the Guy with the Latest Thing hath not where to lay his head. Anyway, I have a website and a blog, though I don't blog as much as I should since the people beseech me so often I can't get to the laptop. I have no need of thee, oh reporter, so get thee hence.

And Matt another wannabe groupie saith, "I can write up thy blog for thee. For lo, I was once the Chief Blogger of Her Majesty's VAT Service but now they have a new software to generate blogs from press releases and no longer am I employed. Suffer me first to go and bury my father and I will writeth thy blog." And, behold, his groupies watched him to see what Bossy would do.

Bossy answereth him and saith, "Let the *Co-op Mortician Service* bury thy father, for thou canst claim it back on the Social. Do thou follow me!" And Matt did as he was bid and took the laptop and began blogging.

Then did Bossy call unto him Jim the son of Alf and did say unto him "Was not thou a school teacher in days gone by?" And Jim agreed that he was before the stinking government cuts did mean that he lost his job. "Then get thee a laptop also," instructeth Bossy. "And monitor thou the newspapers and media and blogs and such. And if so ever a story appeareth that saith anything against us then cometh and tell me of it." And Jim the son of Alf did as he was instructed.

Then was brought unto Bossy one possessed of a spirit of sulkiness, griping and mooning and of great grumpiness. And he taketh him by the hand and commandeth the spirit of negativity and down-beatness to come out of him. And straightaway he falleth about with the giggles and his grin was even like unto the banana split. And Bossy saith unto him, "Get thee on the Radio Two phone-in that all People might hear how thou hast cast away thy down-beatness and displayest the vacuous frivolity which belongeth to all them that are possessed of the Latest Thing."

And straightaway he that was healed of the spirit of grumpiness, lowereth his trousers and flasheth his backside at them which drew nigh. And when they saw this, they did laugh and Percy of the Beeb came forth from the crowd and said, "Yea, I am in the senior management team at the Beeb and behold, verily thou art good enough for that thine appearance may be on the show that is called *I'm A Celebrity: Get Me Out of Egypt* as it is written."

But they all with one voice say unto him, "Why forgettest thou, that which was aforetime Egypt is now Neasden - for remember how it was said of him, 'Egypt - not bloody likely! There's all sand there not human rights, and that!'"

And lo, they all fell about in the spirit of vacuous frivolity as the custom is.

Now when the spirit of grumpiness had come out of the man, one man who was a vicar of the old farts drew near to him and said, "Thou castest out grumpiness by Old Grumpy, the spirit of grumpiness."

Be he saith, "If I by Old Grumpy cast out grumpiness, by whom do thy lot cast it out?"

And they could not answer him to any of these things. And Hack wrote down what he heard, and went abroad in the crowd to collect anecdotes and take photos, as was his wont. But Bossy regardeth not Hack but went up unto Percy of the Beeb and spake unto him flattering words and questioned him closely. And Bossy rejoiced for he found that Percy of the Beeb was consumed with guilt for his wealth and his education and his father having been a rich lawyer withal. And moreover was Percy willing to abase himself to assuage his guilt, as it was said by Jak the Aquatherapist. And Bossy saith "Cleave thee unto me and we shall do great things together."

Now the old farts were exceeding grumpy and down-beat and weary of all the humourless abasements and the modernisation that was throughout all the land. They were even like unto Fogey who loved not the colour supplements which are called *Naff*, and did abhor the music which is Rap and Rock and soundeth out through all the air and ceaseth not by day, and in the night-season giveth no rest.

Chapter Six

In which BOSSY
meeteth MAD
MAGDA

Now when Jak the Aquatherapist heard in the care-in-the-community home the works of Bossy, he sent two of his physios which said unto him, "Art thou he that should come, or look we another?"

Bossy answered and said unto them, "The visually-challenged are wearing strong glasses and the hearing-impaired have their hearing aids. The pimpled are de-pimpled, the semi-comatose malingerers are raised up and the underprivileged and disadvantaged have the gospel of Political-Correctness preached unto them. And chirpy is he whosoever will not get stroppy with me."

And as they departed, Bossy began to say unto the multitudes concerning Jak, "What went ye out to the Serpentine for to see - a toff clothed in a stripy suit? Behold, they that wear stripy suits are in the *Carlton Club*. But what went ye out for to see - a Guru? Yea, I say unto thee, and more than a Guru, for this is he of whom it saith in all the promos and trailers, 'Behold, I send my warm-up man before thy face which shall prepare the audience before thou comest on.'

"Verily I say unto thee, among them that have ministered the therapy which is called 'alternative', there hath not risen a greater than Jak.

"But whereunto shall I liken this generation? It is like unto children sitting in the amusement arcades and calling to their mates, 'We gave you the *iPod* but you would not dance.'

"For Jak came not dancing and they say he hath the spirit of grumpiness. But the Guy with the Latest Thing came dancing and thou sayest, 'Behold, a piss-artist utterly arseholed, a mate of publicans and twenty-four hour boozing!'"

46

At that time the Prime Bureaucrat who Knew Not What He Did heard of the fame of Bossy and was wroth. And he calleth his apparatchiks and saith, "This is Jak the Aquatherapist escaped from the Special Needs Unit!"

And, behold, the wife of the Prime Bureaucrat who Knew Not What He Did was named Berenice and claimed to be a victim of the psychopathic syndrome. But others say, "Sod that - she's a mean cow and a raving nutter!" Moreover Jak the Aquatherapist had treated her lover Costa Barus for dodgy knees, and so learned of the love Costa bore for Berenice. And Jak had blabbed the story to the Sunday papers.

Now when the Prime Bureaucrat's birthday was kept, Polony, the daughter of Berenice - she of the cleavage like unto the Cave of Machpelah - danced before them and pleased the Prime Bureaucrat. So that the Bureaucrat did promise with an oath, saying, "Bloody hell! Look at the tits on yon bint!" to give her whatsoever she wouldst, up to the half of all the juicy contracts given to his building company by the Eurocrat his friend in return for having no truck with the referendum thing. And Polony, being instructed of Berenice her mother, saith, "Send Jak the Aquatherapist to the looney bin."

And when he heard this the Prime Bureaucrat was bummed out. Nevertheless, for his oath's sake and for the sake of them that sat in the disco with him, he commanded that a tame psychologist in the pay of the government be sent unto the Special Needs Unit to reclassify Jak as being well round the twist. And so it was done.

And when Bossy heard of it, he departed thence into the country round about Dagenham.

And when he had called unto him the twelve groupies, he gave them skills against the psychoneuroses, the fashionable ailments and all manner of imaginary diseases among the People: the *acne vulgaris* (which hath aforetime been called pimples), the ME and the post-traumatic stress disorder, the Munchausen

Syndrome by Proxy, the Narcissistic Personality Disorder, spurious allergic reactions, anorexia nervosa (which is called in their language "the attention-seeking throwing-up syndrome")' sundry forms of malingering and divers kinds of "stress".

Now the names of the twelve are these: the first Sim (or Simmy) which is called Pete; Andy his brother; Jim the son of Zeb; and Jon (not the Aquatherapist); Randy Phil, Bart, Tom and Matty the VAT man; Jim the son of Alf (which in the days of their political-incorrectness was called "the cripple") and Jude the Obscure (for he told nobody where he came from). There were also among his groupies a great many sheilas, some of them right old slappers. And Randy Phil and Tom and Jim the son of Alf and others did enjoy the slappers, but not Bossy for he preached that slappers were humans too and had their human rights and deserved dignity. He appointeth a right old mixed bag for to bear witness that he chooseth his groupies irrespective of race, gender, sexual orientation or disability.

About this time Bossy and his groupies went down unto Romford to establish a Centre for Political Correctness, wherein the deserving could attend courses and lessons and pay therefore. And the centre was to be complete with the organic restaurant wherein were served exquisite dishes of marvellous tastiness and wondrous cost, and with bedrooms of great starkness wherein visitors could savour of the simple life while paying through the nose, and with many chambers wherein could be held seminars for the enlightenment of the righteous. And lo, Bossy did find a derelict place of worship, close unto the railway station, not far from the A12 and with its own car park, and with some houses out back that was wondrous to his eyes.

"Behold," he told his groupies. "This is where we shall establish the realm of righteousness for the benefit of all." Then did he proclaim to the Council that the buildings were of excellent Victorian design such as the truly enlightened of artistic genius could see were worth preserving and only the wickedly capitalist would want

to demolish. And he did send a text to Sebastian that read "I've found the perfect place. Get down here pdq and don't pay too much as they daren't flog it for demolition now."

As the sun set Bossy and his groupies went unto the Ship Inn to partake of the fine foods and drinks that are to be found there. And when Tom the groupie went off to the gents, lo his place at Bossy's side was taken by a blonde of ample cleavage and a knowing look who saith "Hello Bossy. How's the cash flow going?" And she gave the wink. Then Bossy did look at her askance, but she said "Nice little earner you've got yourself. But you're missing a trick or two - I'll soon show you. Cut me in, love, and we'll both be rolling in it. Us and that Sebastian bloke you pretend you don't know."

And Bossy did produce a wadge of notes and bade his groupies go and order themselves the dish known in Romford as 'the all day breakfast', verily even that with two eggs, two sausages, two rashers and the fried bread. And he did speak with the blonde, whose name was Magda, known as Mad Magda down Romford way for her marvellously awful temper.

And when the Centre for Political Correctness was completed Bossy summoned all his groupies and he sent them forth - except Mad Magda who he kept close - and commanded them, saying, "Go not to Scotland, nor into that country wherein they that are called 'Taffs'; but go ye rather to the politically-incorrect of the nation that is England for they are the ones with the money.

"And as ye go say, 'Behold, Cloud Cuckoo Land is at hand with all manner of modernisation.' Counsel the neurotic, cleanse their pimples, humour the suggestible, raise them that have the hysterical paralysis (which were formerly the malingerers) and cast out he psychoneuroses and all manner of dietary and health fads. And in all these things see ye that ye pay due and honourable service to Quality Assurance and all manner of Compliance. And remember to tell them always that they can pay via our website using all major credit cards and debit cards.

"Take neither purse nor scrip, neither any credit card, ready or cheque book; for behold, there is a rich living to be made out of the suckers which pay for all this attention.

"And into any health department ye enter, enquire of him or her that is called Head of Centre, and abide with him or her until ye go hence.

"And when ye come into an house, disinfect it and see ye do the Feng Shui according to the word that was spoken unto you by the Gurus. And whosoever shall not pay thee for thy therapy, thy counselling and thy Feng Shui, tell them that verily they get not this sort of treatment on the NHS. And tell them that they will be damned among their fellows for being agents of the Politically Incorrect evil, until such time as they pay via

our website when they will be counted among the righteous.

"Behold, I send you forth as caring agents among the stiff upper lips. Be ye therefore as skilled as stress counsellors and as euphemistic as psychotherapists.

"But beware of Fogey and them that watch his chat show, even that which is on ITV, and them that listen to his radio show for they be not modernised. For they will mock you and tell jokes about you in bad taste. They will deliver thee up to their pubs and clubs, and finally they will set thee at nought and satirise thee.

"But when they bring you into their pubs and clubs for to mock you, take no thought for what ye shall say, for lo, the Latest Thing shall give you utterance and ye shall answer them unto their mockery and their satirising out of the Standard Practice, the Manual of Compliance and the Laws of Political-Correctness which shall never be removed."

And he saith unto them in his doctrine, "Are not two sparrows protected by the RSPB? Ye are of more value than many sparrows - and here's the Certification of Competence to prove it.

"Whoso therefore shall be a groupie of mine, he shall be also a groupie of the Latest Thing. For the Latest Thing and I are an item. But whosoever shall not do as the Latest Thing commandeth, shall feel a right Charlie when the Latest Thing doth appear in all its glory.

"For I am come to set a man at variance against his father, and the daughter against her mother. And thine enemies shall be thine own household. And any child that loveth his or her father and mother more than he or she loveth Political Correctiness, shall be removed from thence. And, behold, I send before thee Social Workers and divers of that which is called 'Inspectorate', and they shall take thee from that place unto a place of Political-Correctness as the Standard Practice hath commanded them.

"And verily all shall be done that is Politically Correct, for this is for the good of all whether they know it or not, whether they want it or not. For I know what is best and you groupies know what is best. For remember the Truth is greater than the Facts."

And the groupies departed from the railway station to the far corners of the kingdom. And Bossy and Mad Magda got down to staffing the Centre for Political Correctness, the same that Magda said had to be young ladies of obvious charms, and to setting forth the politically correct content of the seminars, and to finding ways to make the righteous feel that they were truly enlightened so that they were superior to the chavs and old farts. Verily even did Sebastian come down to Romford for to set up a secure payment software system of hideous complexity that would hide the trail of payments that ended up in Bermuda from the eyes of the taxman.

And yet they did not spy Hack in the Ship the while.

Chapter Seven

In which
BOSSY goeth
unto KENT

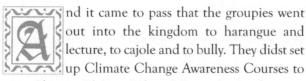nd it came to pass that the groupies went out into the kingdom to harangue and lecture, to cajole and to bully. They didst set up Climate Change Awareness Courses to train Climate Change Policy Officers for employment by councils to enforce rules on the unenlightened and to heap praise in the press on those who switch off their lights at night, yea even though passersby fall over and break their legs. They didst establish Anti-Racism Awareness Courses to ensure that people knowest that a miscreant was racist, even if that miscreant knew it not themselves. And they performed many other miracles whereby the joys of political correctness were brought to those who wanted it not.

And so after this time the groupies returned unto the Centre for Political Correctness (staffed by young ladies of obvious charms) and did marvel at the throngs of the righteous that were attending seminars and awareness courses with their credit cards in hand.

And Bossy constrained his groupies to get into a boat and go before him unto the other side of the Estuary unto Kent, peradventure he would come upon them ere the sun was risen. And with them went a crew from the Beeb sent unto them by Percy of the Beeb to film a slot for the Evening News on the renewal of righteousness in Kent. But when the ship was now in the midst of the estuary, it was tossed with waves, for the wind was contrary.

And, behold, he came unto them walking on water. When the groupies saw him walking on the water, they were freaked out and some they kitteneth and Bart saith, "It's a ghost - like unto that one we watched in that movie in Southend, *The Lady in White*. Remember ye it?"

And Matt saith, "Thou meanest that movie with the damsel that is called Sharon Stone, wherin she crosseth and uncrosseth her legs, and verily we get an eyeful of her - "

"Of a surety it was not that movie, for that was called Basic Instinct and I do believe it also starred Michael

Douglas and the damsel Stone hath said, when the movie was ended, that verily the scenes of lust be so marvelous in their configuration that she and Douglas were 'the horizontal Fred and Ginger of the 1990s'. And lo, there appeareth no spook in it."

Whereupon, Pete was wroth and greatly angered and saith, "Cut the crap ye two! For it appeareth like unto Bossy which walketh on the water." And the TV crew did filmeth it.

And Bossy calleth to them, saying, "Be thou not freaked out, for it is I! Behold my new act which I do prepare that the multitudes might go, 'Ooh!' for they believe it happeneth some great sign and wonder. But the great number of Scribes that be of the Deconstructionist Party which come after shall say, "Think not that this be a sign, but a pericope of the salvific narrative and verily no more than *une parole* in the langue which is called *mysthos*."

And Pete crieth out in a loud voice and saith,

"Facilitator, I would be of thy periscope and thy salvific narrative which they that be of the Deconstructionist Party do preach. For lo, I have made a long reading of the *Gesamtkrisistheologie* in the scroll that is *Wissenschaft fur Einen Neuen Zeitgeist* that even I also might bore the very arse off any of them that listen." And straightaway, Pete jumpeth over the side and floundereth.

And they all with one voice began to call out, "He's fallen in the wa-ter!" And do laugh him to scorn.

But Bossy upbraided them for their hardness of heart and taketh Pete by the hand and raiseth him up saying, "Thou wilt have to practice a lot more, lad, before thou canst enter this pericope - nay not a periscope thou oaf. For this Deconstruction cometh only after much of that which is called 'smoke and mirrors'.

Mind you if the Mayor with the Mop Hair buildeth his island airport I may need a new stunt for the cameras."

And the TV crew filmeth not this last bit for lo they had been instructed by Percy of the Beeb, their boss, "maketh Bossy look good or you'll be back in a tropical swamp filming wild life documentaries so fast your feet won't touch the floor". Then did Kevin the Cameraperson say unto Bernie the Soundperson "That Bossy is as mad as a hatter, and very bossy withal."

"Verily," replieth Bernie. "But the missus wants a foreign holiday this year and so I need the work. We'll have to do what Percy says, you know that he be a bastard most vindictive." And so they nodded and compromised and did as they were instructed.

And in the morning when Bossy and his groupies were landed in Kent, even in Whitstable, behold, his groupies come unto him in the oyster and champagne bar - where Bossy was dining for the benefit of his delicate digestive system on doctor's orders - and say, "Moderniser General, tell us what meaneth thy riddles for the secret of their words is hid from us, neither understand we thy jargon."

"No problem," he saith.

Hear ye therefore the spin of the sower. The sower is the Guru or it happeneth the counsellor or even him which is called the therapist.

"When anyone heareth the modern message, that which belongeth to Cloud Cuckoo Land or which telleth of the perfect life for all People which shall be delivered by Political Correctness, but that person saith that, behold, the promo is but bullshit and that all the modernising initiatives be but crap, this is the seed that fell by the wayside.

"But they that receive the spin and the initiatives in stony places, these are they which heareth the bullshit (sorry - thou forgive me, a false word hath slipped from my lips: I say rather not the bullshit but the modernising) and at once thinketh it cool and verily the latest thing since sliced supernatural sandwiches. Yet these have no root, for they have not received the

appropriate training, neither the education in the gospel of political correctness; and when Fogey appears on the television or radio and does mock them and satirise them and say, as it might be, 'Hast thou heard the latest? It's bloody crackers! And verily thou couldst not make it up,' they are offended and fall away from the coolness of the modernising which they have heard, and loseth their cutting edge.

"They that recieve the gospel of modernisation among thorns are they which hearken unto it positively but are tempted away by the fogeyishness and reconstructed conservatism which speaketh of the good old days and are led away, as it happeneth, unto the *Carlton Club* or the cricket ground which is called *Lord's*. These are they that recieve the gospel of modernisation among thorns.

"But they that are effectively trained in all the relevant training courses (of the which there are legion at the Centre for Political Correctness, bring your credit card), and that have their consciousness raised by the education which is Politically-Correct, these are they that do reinvent themselves and do stick posters in the windows of their houses as a promo for Bossy and all his works. This is the seed which has falleth on good ground."

And the groupies saith unto him, "Now thou speakest plain and thy riddles are no riddles and thy jargon be dejargonified before our eyes and lo, we will serve the moderisation all the days of our life."

"Yeah," saith Andy, "we've really swallowed the bullshit!" And he addeth, "Just testing - that be all. Just testing!" And they began to fall all about that place in their laughter.

In those days cometh Bossy unto his own town, even unto Southend. And he did give presentations in the Health Centre there, insomuch that they were freaked out and said, "Whence hath this man this slickness? Behold, he is smooth, and even very smooth. Is not this the son of Wayne, the hoodie, and Rubella his mother, which is called 'the randy' so that verily she is forever up the duff? And are not these here his brethren, Darren and Trev and Lee and Kevin? And his sisters Mean and Amber, which are called 'slags'?

"Whence then hath this man this pizzazz and this sexiness?"

But the Sarfenders declared, "Where's he get his ego, then?"

And they were pissed off with him.

But he saith, "A Guru is a big star except on his own midden and his own manor."

And Bossy could do no "spin" there. For they believed not in his street cred. And so he returned unto Romford, yea even unto Mad Magda who was viewing houses in the green fields by Stapleford Abbotts. There they did find an abode of great luxury, even unto a private swimming pool. And they saw not Hack among the hills.

Chapter Eight

In which BOSSY goeth to MARGATE

nd, behold, they that were of the old farts drew near and asked him, saying, "Why do thy groupies devour burgers in the streets and dine not in the *Carlton Club*?"

But Bossy answereth them, "Why art thou and thy groupies so passe, antique and even elitist? Is not the scoff, which is given thee of the Latest Thing, greater than where thou scoffest it? I perceive that in all things thou art uncool."

And they durst not ask him any more questions, save that they condemned him because of the burgers, saying that they were oafish and oikish.

But he saith unto them, "Not that which goeth into the mouth giveth street cred to a guy, but that which cometh out of the mouth when thou art on the *Stella*.

"And when thou goest forth on the binge, see that thou bingest greatly, so that they that be with thee say, 'Jesus - verily he doth get a lot down his neck!'

"Then that which thou dost get down thy neck shall proceed outward again even through the mouth and thou shalt throw up exceedingly. Then shall thy gut be ready the second time to recieve what thou bingest. And they shall say, 'Verily that lad hath got no clack!'

"Then shalt thou have honour among them that binge with thee and which, as Fogey says, do throw up 'all over the sodding street and they ought to be horsewhipped and put in the stocks'."

And Bossy went from thence into the country around Islington and Camden. And, behold, a woman of Camden cometh out of *Waitrose* and saith unto him, "Have mercy on me thou Son of Dave; my daughter is grievously vexed with the Princess Di Syndome.

And, behold, she hath the *bulimia* and dreameth at nights and in the daytime also of that which is called 'landmines'. Moreover she saith 'Yah' all day long and in the night season also. And if it so happeneth that any man bring unto her a book, her tongue saith it be a 'buwerck'; and if he ask of her to take a look, she openeth her mouth but a little space and saith 'luwerk'.

"And, behold, she looketh ever to the ground while she raiseth her eyes, so that the aunties do look upon her and say, 'What a trollop! See how she simpereth!'"

"And - "

But Bossy saith, "Woman hold thy peace! Verily I am already persuaded that thy daughter hath the legion of devils. She hath the abundance of nuttiness to make he whole fruitcake - even unto a great fruitcake."

And his groupies say among themselves,

"What a frigging tart this one! This'll test his therapeutic skill all right!"

But he, knowing what was in their hearts, saith, "Leave her alone - for her daughter is grievously tormented."

And, behold, her mother saith, "Oh no, you've got it wrong there. It's not her that's tormented. She loves all the fuss. It's *me* she drives mad!"

And he saith, "This kind cometh out only with much prayer and fasting."

The woman saith unto him, "She don't do no fasting. She stuffeth herself like there's no tomorrow, like, then throws it all up. And she don't pray - not as such. She's got these New Age Counsellors, see!"

When Bossy heard these words he was wroth and saith unto the woman concerning the new Age Counsellors, "Not everyone that calleth himself or herself 'New Age Counsellor' is a

New Age Counsellor. Behold, he or she hath need to submit himself or herself to that which is called 'the three-week professional training course' that is available at the Centre for Political Correctness down east in Romford. Then shall he or she put up the plate on his or her door and be called 'New Age Counsellor'; and receive unto himself or herself the riches thereof."

And the woman entreateth him with great sorrow, "Sir, come and take a butcher's at my daughter."

But he answered and said, "Call no man 'Sir'. For that be elitist. Neither speak thou any more of 'butchers'. For it is written, 'Thou shalt go veggie and even vegan,'"

And he saith, "Moreover, thou dwellest in Camden and I am sent but to the lost sheep of the house of Southend."

But she was exceeding wroth and rent her garments and with a loud voice saith unto him, "There aren't many sodding sheep in Southend, mate!"

And all the groupies did fall about.

Then Bossy chucketh the woman under the chin and saith, "Thou hast answered to all things well. I have not seen such *chutzpah* - no, not even on my holiday in Eilat. Go thy way. Thy feistiness sufficeth." And her daughter was made clean of the Princess Di Syndrome in that self-same hour.

Then Bossy and his groupies departed from London Victoria and went out towards the coasts of Ramsgate and Margate. Then did Bossy say, "On Margate sands I can connect nothing with nothing."

And the groupies say unto one another, "What is this 'Margate sands' of which he speaketh? And that he can connect 'nothing with nothing'? Behold, we cannot tell what he saith."

But he answered, "How is it that ye know not of that I do speak? Behold, I say unto you, these sands which thou calleth 'Margate' shall lie desolate and the whole land shall be waste."

And no man durst ask him any more questions. But Matt saith, "It appeareth the Moderniser General is tormented by the devil of elitism. Send ye therefore for the wireless and play unto him that which is called *Poetry Please*. Verily that knocketh out of him the elitism."

And when they came unto Margate, by the very whelk stall and the amusements that be in the arcade there, Bossy saith unto them, "Whom do the punters say that I, the Son of Wayne, am?"

And they say, "Some say that thou art Jak the Aquatherapist come back from the loony bin; some the prophet Karl Marx, or Stalin which was called Joe."

He saith unto them, "But who say ye that I am?"

And Simmy answered and said, "Thou art the Facilitator, the Moderniser General, the Boy with the Latest Thing."

And Bossy answered and said unto him, "Smart of thee, Simmy. For neither the horoscope in The Star hath revealed this unto the, nor the *Old Moore's Almanack*; but the Latest Thing in Cloud Cuckoo Land. And I say also unto thee that thou art Pete and upon this rock star I will build my Project; and the forces of conservatism shall not prevail against it, neither Fogey nor they that are yesterday's news. And I will give thee the PIN number of Cloud Cuckoo Land: and whatsoever thou shalt ban in all the Nanny State shall be banned in Cloud Cuckoo Land until the Great Modernisation be complete."

Then charged he his groupies that they should tell no one that he was the Guy with the Latest Thing.

From that time forth Bossy began to show his groupies how that he must go to the Great City and suffer lousy notices and score zilch in the opinion polls, and have the piss taken out of him by Fogey and be patronised. Even that he would be satirised. But that after three days he would be known as the Comeback Kid.

Then Pete took him and began to chew him out, saying, "Be it far from thee, Moderniser General, to be satirised and patronised and have the piss taken out of thee. These things shall not be done unto thee - not while I'm in charge of the promos!"

But Bossy turned and said unto him, "Get thee behind

me, Pete! - for thou art an offence to me. For thou savourest not which parts of the Project are the Latest Thing, but which are, like, yucky and unreconstructed!"

And he saith, "If any guy backs my Project and, like, is on my bandwagon, let him get wasted for my sake. And let him be patronised and satirised and have the piss taken. For whosoever will lose his street cred for my sake and the sake of the Project shall find it. For what is a guy profited if he shall get all the promos and the fab notices but lose his image? Or what shall a guy give in exchange for his iconic status? And the Guy with the Latest Thing shall come in the Glitz of the Latest Thing with his Vibes and Archvibes; and all his groupies and cronies shall receive their payoff.

"But verily I say unto you, there be guys standing here which shall not have the piss taken or even be satirised until they have seen the Guy with the Latest Thing accomplish the Great Modernisation."

Then did Jim the son of Alf come to Bossy and say "Behold this newspaper article I have called up. It saith that climate change is just natural variability and nothing to be frightened of and that we should mine our shale gas to reduce power bills for the masses."

And Bossy readeth the piece saying "It even says that wind turbines kill rare birds and bats."

"Verily that is true," sayeth Jim for I checked it out, like.

And Bossy giveth him orders saying "Report the journalist who wrote this tosh to the Press Complaints Commission. Telleth them that everything he writes is untrue and libellous and politically incorrect to boot. They will require him to justify his piece and to prove all the statement that we say are untrue. That should keep the bastard busy for a couple of days and stop him working."

"But Bossy," quoth Jim. "What he writes is true for I have been surfing and reading the blogs of the Bishop Hill and of Delingpole and others. And verily the increased cost of electricity caused by the feed in tariffs and other subsidies doth cause old ladies to turn off their heating in the snows and they do hyperthermise unto death. "

"Do not come unto me with facts," saith Bossy. "For the Truth is greater than the facts. And the Truth is that we must cut down on carbon emissions for the benefit of our souls and of Gaia. Do as I say. Then when he has wasted his time and proved his facts, write thou again to the Press Complaints Commission and demand a right of reply. That will keep him busy again and waste his time such that he can neither write more such pieces nor earn money. And also write thee to his editor to denounce him as a troublemaker and a man who denies science and is in the pay of big oil companies. Yea and write ye unto all the companies that advertise in this paper to tell them likewise and accuse them of being in the pay of big oil and of being an enemy of humankind for denying the reality of climate change by advertising in this rag. Thus will we enforce our censorship of the press such that only that which is Politically Correct will be printed."

And Jim the son of Alf did as he was bid. And lo it came to pass.

Chapter Nine

In which BOSSY INVENTS a RACIST

hen cometh Bossy unto the City and behold, a junior partner in one of the law firms there, tempting him, saith, "Moderniser, what shall I do to be totally Politically-Correct?"

And he saith, "What is written in the Project? How readest thou?"

And he, answering, saith, "Thou shalt love the Latest Thing even to die for. And fawn over complete strangers and people you've never bloody-well heard of with all thy mawkishness."

And he said unto him, "Thou hast answered like unto the perfect new man and with ace street cred. This do and thou shalt be altogether Politcally-Correct."

But he, pedantic, stiff necked and hard of heart (as it be with the lawyers) saith, "And who is the complete stranger and person I've never bloody-well heard of?"

Bossy, answering, saith "This guy went down from Chelsea to Dagenham and, as he passed through the East End, fell among hoodies and muggers which stripped him of his designer clobber and pissed off leaving him, like, duffed up. And, by chance, there came down a certain man which profiteth by the tobacco industry that way, and when he saw the guy he passed by on the other side. And likewise a four-by-four owner who, it happened, was also an international arms dealer, when he was at the place, came and looked on him and passed by on the other side.

"But a certain social worker which worketh for the equal opportunities among the disadvantaged and them that are gay and vulnerable in the deprived inner city, when she journeyed came where he was and went to him. And she was a lesbian. And she sticketh on a sticky plaster and giveth him the Echinacea and, behold, she saith, 'Verily the person that hath done this is a victim which needeth professional help!' And she shoved him in the back of the *Volvo* and taketh him to the hostel for them that be the underprivileged - which were aforetime the dossers, the shiftless wonders and the layabouts - and handeth a pile of tokens and vouchers to the do-

gooder which doeth good there and saith, 'See that thou compliest with all that be in accordance with health and safety and do thou take care for, for any forms which thou fillest not in threefold thou shalt receive bollockings double for all thy non-compliance.'

"Which now of these three thinkest thou was mawkish to the one that fell among thieves and was exceeding sentimental over him?"

Then the lawyer saith, "The lesbian social worker - even she that doeth Political-Correctness unto him that fell among hoodies."

Bossy saith, "Go and do thou likewise."

But the lawyer saith, "Look, mate, I just wanna be Politically-Correct! I'm not going to go about giving cash to dossers for you or anyone else." And he passed on.

And as the lawyer passed on Bossy summoned Matt unto him and saith "Behold this man that spurneth me and receiveth not the good news that is Political Correctness, and behold his child. What seeth thou?"

And Matt looked and saith "I see a little girl aged about four with plaits and a rucksack. So what?"

Then did Bossy rebuke him saying "Thou see, but thou dost not see. Look at the rucksack for poking out the top is a doll of the type known as gollywog, a thing of loathsome political incorrectness. Now get out thy laptop, link up and begin blogging. Thou must denounce this lawyer as a racist pig, and his firm as a business dabbling with the evil of racism, and all his kin as being kin to a racist. And get his business details off Company House and do ye email all the directors and shareholders to denounce this man as a racist. And tell them that if they sack him not I shall denounce them as closet racists and that we shall name them on a programme made by Percy of the Beeb. For this lawyer we must destroy utterly."

And Matt looked surprised and saith "But its only the kid's doll, for gawd's sake. Why the fuss?"

Then did Bossy grow wroth saying "It is not the doll, thou fool amongst fools. This lawyer did turn his back on us and so he must be destroyed and his career trodden underfoot and his relatives turned against him. Then will others fear to turn their backs on us lest we destroy them also. Those that we cannot win to our cause, we will bully to our cause and those we cannot bully to our cause we will destroy. Thus will Political Correctness triumph. We must be cruel to be kind, for it is best for all to be Politically Correct whether they want to or not.

Then did Matt blog and email as he was instructed so that the lawyer might be destroyed and his political incorrectness with him.

And after six days Bossy taketh Pete, Jim and Jon and bringeth them to the press conference. And, behold, he really sparkled and dazzled and his face shone in The Sun when they did the photo-shoot; and his gear was white as anything worn by that man which is called Martin Bell. And, behold, there came to sit with Bossy at the press conference the President of the EU and the Secretary-General of the UN. And all three did speak to the peoples of the world saying that the world must be anti-racist, must be anti-carbon, must be anti-greed and in favour all things politically correct.

And the groupies were freaked out. Then Pete saith unto him, "This is what it's all about, eh? Let's take over three studios - one for thee, one for the President and the other for the Secretary General. We could run the world from here!"

While he yet spake, the strobe lights flashed and the captions rolled and the link man went into the big promo, "And now let's hear it for the Moderniser General!" And lo, they all kitteneth.

But Bossy saith, "Have ye no kittens. I'm just practising!"

At the same time, came the groupies unto Bossy and asked him, "Who shall be most famous when the Final Dianafication shall come?"

And Bossy calleth a TV presenter with a voice like unto a little child and set him in the midst of them and saith, "Except ye become babyish and like, totally infantilised, ye cannot enter on the Dianafication.

"Whosoever shall gurgle and coo and affect utter childishness and gather unto themselves soft toys - as it happeneth the teddy bear or some of those Smurfs that be handed out on *Children in Need* - the same shall be greatest in the Dianafication.

"But whoso shall offend one of these totally infantilised air heads and commandeth her or him, 'Grow up!' it were better for them that balloons were hanged about their necks and they were sent to the naughty corner."

And Pete cometh to him and saith, "Facilitator, we know that thou art clued up more than anybody when it cometh to the Standard Practice, and that, behold of all the that be Politically Correct and completely modernised, there is none more Politically Correct nor modernised than thee. Tell us, how oft shall my neighbour offend me before I sue him? Till seven times?"

And he saith, "I say not unto thee seven times, but seventy times seven. For is it not written in the Standard Practice, 'Thou shalt shop thy neighbour as thyself'? For verily, if thou findest that thou thyself offend against what is in the Standard Practice and shalt see thyself on *Crimewatch*, thou shalt surrender thyself to the Politically-Correct Police."

Then came a man from out of Liverpool who was bored of his wife, who did ask, "Facilitator, is it lawful for a man to put away his wife for any cause?"

And he saith, "Have ye not read how the Latest Thing hath made an offence discrimination on the grounds of gender? How say ye then of these things which be no more, for verily they are all modernised, these things 'man' and 'woman' of which ye speak?

"For according to the Latest Thing, a man or a woman shall leave his or her mother and father - or as it happeneth her or his one-parent family (for that her or his dad hath done a runner or her or his old lady getteth pissed off and shacketh up with her lesby girlfriend) and move in with any tosser he or she lusteth after. And this thing shall be called 'a relationship'.

"But and if she or he waxeth bored of her or his new partner, then she or he split and go forth seeking someone else to shag. For the children of Modern Britain are not given in marriage, save if it happeneth they be gay which constantly beseech the Prime Bureaucrat that they might marry and not be in a civil partnership.

"What therefore the Latest Thing hath joined together, let any woman or man put asunder."

And a woman cometh to him out of Arundel and saith, "Fab Moderniser General, what shall I do that I may be cool and Politically-Correct?"

And he saith, "Why callest thou me 'Fab'? There is none fab but the Latest Thing. But if thou wouldst be cool and enter into that life which is Politically-Correct, thou shalt keep the statuses and ordinances which are in the Standard Practice. Thou shalt not be racist, neither shalt thou be sexist and thou shalt seek equal opportunities on a non-discriminatory basis all the days of thy life."

The young woman saith unto him, "All these statutes and ordinances have I kept since the first day of my modernisation when I did enter the re-education course decreed by the Nanny State. What further evidence of compliance need I?"

And Bossy said, "One thing thou lackest: give greatly of thy substance unto *Red Nose Day* or, as it happeneth, *Children in Need* and thou shalt have kudos amongst them that are modernised."

But when the young man heard this saying, he went away sorrowing - for he loveth not in his heart the mawkishness of *Red Nose Day*, neither the humourless abasements which are that which is called *Children in Need*.

Chapter Ten

In which BOSSY forgiveth LOOPINESS

nd Bossy goeth the third time to the region round about the Serpentine and, behold, his groupies were with him. And also went there Percy of the Beeb with his anchor man and his camera operator (for lo, though he was a man the job description 'cameraman' was politically incorrect and was banned). And when all was set and the camera in place and the lighting just so, Bossy began to teach them concerning role models, saying, "A certain man which dwelleth in Hampstead had two sons. And the younger of them said unto his father, 'Give me the portion of goods that falleth to me that I may go unto Brighton and get totally wrecked and shag everything that moveth,'

"And his father saith, 'Be it unto thee even as thou desirest.'

"And not many days hence the younger son gathered all together and took his journey into Brighton wherein he did get totally wrecked and lo, he shaggeth everything that moveth, whether man or woman or beast or creeping thing that creepeth over the face of the earth, on a completely non-discriminatory basis.

"And when he had spent all, there was a downturn in the bond market and he was cleaned out. And, behold, he went and dossed with them that do doss, even with the druggies, the alcys and them that were two sandwiches short of a miraculous picnic, being like, totally out of it on the meths and that which is called 'glue'.

"And he would fain have filled his belly with the remnants of the junk food cartons which the yobbos do cast down all over the frigging place. And none in that town would render unto him even so much as the cellophane off his *ciabatta*.

"And when he came to himself he saith, 'How many *au pairs* and cleaning ladies in my father's house in Hamstead have *ciabatta* and *guacamole* enough and to spare, and I fall faint with the druggies, the alcys and them that be two sandwiches short of a miraculous picnic?'

"Behold, I am purposed what I will do. I will arise and go to the old feller and say unto him: Dad, I've screwed up big time and am no more worthy to be called thy son. Make me as one of thy cleaning ladies or even like unto one of the *au pairs* in thine household which peradventure my elder brother yet screweth.'

"And he arose and hitcheth along the A23 until he cometh to the South Circular Road, whence he taketh shank's pony even unto Hampstead.

"But when he was yet a great way off, behold, his elder brother seeth him and saith unto his father, 'Behold, that sodding waster's back - him that did bugger off unto Brighton and getteth totally wrecked these many months, and shaggeth everything that moveth non-discriminatingly as to whether it be man or woman or beast or creepy thing that creepeth over the face of the whole earth.'

"But his father saith, 'Bring forth the designer clobber and put it on him and bring hither that fatted calf and kill it. And let there be a disco and other such noisome filth. For this my son hath gone forth and asserted his own identity and distanced himself from the narrow confines of the family unit, and he now returneth a mature person with his own self-esteem.'

"But the hired caterers say unto him, 'Lo, there is no fatted calf for (thou must remember, thou silly nod) we all went veggie according as the Latest Thing hath commanded us. Besides, the

EU directeth long ago that slaughter of animals wast prohibited under section 36 of the European Food, Health and Safety Regulations.'

"And his father saith, 'Ye have spoken rightly. What the hell was I thinking about!'

"And he commandeth that they bring forth the nut roast and rocket salad.

"Now his elder brother was on the patio and, as he drew nigh into the house, he heard the noise of disco. And he calleth one of the au pairs and enquired as to what manner of salutation this might be. And she saith unto him, 'C'est le pillock thy kid frere qui est retrouve, comme, apres he screweth around, comme, touts les mois sans-discrimination, homme, femme, bete ou les escargots a Brighton et touts-les-points sud.'

"And he was wroth and would not enter into the disco. Therefore came out unto him his father and saith, 'Sulk thou not, thou anal-retentive prat! For thou hast never gone out so much as one night on the piss, nor discoverest thou for thyself thy identity or thy role; neither hast thou any self-esteem. Rejoice with me, for thy brother wast screwed up even as thou art. But behold, he findeth his image and hath become an icon and a role model and verily he is filled with self-esteem.'"

Then cometh Bossy into the City and seeth all the brokers and traders which return from their third charlie break that morning and do take care over their sojourn and ease in faraway countries with their concubines and partners.

And he saith, "Behold, how hardly shall a capitalist or he that worshipped the globalised economy enter into Cloud Cuckoo Land! It is easier for a pantomime horse to go limbo dancing beneath the loo door than for a capitalist to enter into Cloud Cuckoo Land."

And his groupies say unto him, "Who, then, can achieve personal fulfillment?"

He saith, "With persons this is impossible, but with the Latest Thing all things are possible."

Then Pete saith, "Lo, we have given up all to follow the Latest Thing, what shall be in it for us, therefore?"

He saith, "Verily I say unto thee, that ye which have followed the Latest Thing on Earth shall, when the Great Modernisation be accomplished and Political-Correctness shall rule throughout the land, sit in the Parliament of the European Superstate - where the expenses are wondrous lavish - and shall be called 'Bossy' even as I am Bossy."

And Percy of the Beeb did say "That was great oh Bossy. I'll make sure it gets on the News, and News Evening will want a clip. Doeth thou interviews?"

"Yea, verily," replieth Bossy. "But not with that Stuffing bloke, he asketh really tricky questions."

"Worry ye not," saith Percy of the Beeb. "Thou shalt have easy questions and a soft intro, I reserveth difficult questions for those who speaketh not the creed of the Politically Correct. And those that do not as I wish, truly do I sack them and terminate their contracts. And those that are left do as I bid for very fear of my wrath and of the sacking."

Then it came to pass the day after that he went into a town named Cheam and many of his groupies went with him and much people. And when he came nigh unto *The Cemetery Tavern* a paralytic man was carried out, the only son of his single mother, for behold, his father hath done a runner before he was born and the Child Support Agency findeth him not.

And when Bossy saw the single mother he was minded to interfere whether she liketh it or no. So he came and touched the beery one. And they that were his brethren and acquaintance stood still. Then he saith unto him that wast paralytic, "Arise!"

And he that was, like, totally out of it, stood up and saith, "Pint o' *Stella*"

Then delivered he him to his single mother and she saith, "O God - and I thought I was going to get some peace and quiet from that one this afternoon!"

And they all freaked out and said, "He hath done all things well. He maketh both the old farts to get the hump and the totally arseholed to get more down their necks!" Then they departed into *The Cemetery Tavern* for the hour that is called "Blessed Hour".

And one of those a man in a grey suit who was of the party of the Prime Bureaucrat desireth Bossy that he would dine with him in the *Carlton Club*. And he went into the *Carlton Club* and did sit down at meat with him - for the fish it wast "off".

And, behold, one of the women who ran the Alternative Therapy and Holistic Counselling shop down Jermyn Street, when she knew that Bossy wast eating fish with the politicians, brought an alabaster box with her aromatherapy. And, her eyes watering for the niff of the garlic that was there, began to administer to him the specimen trial course of her aromatherapy. She taketh also his feet and practiseth her reflexology there.

And the man which had bidden him to the *Carlton Club* - Simmy (not Pete) - began to say, "Send her away! For this is that weirdo from down Jermyn Street and, behold, she hath the iniquities of the New Age like unto the very devil!"

But Bossy, answering, said unto him, "Simmy, I have some-what to say unto thee!"

And he, willing to justify himself , saith, "Facilitator, say on."

And Bossy opened his mouth and saith, "There was a barfly in the *Carlton Club* which paid the bar bills of two old boys from his school: the one of three score Euros and the other an hundred. And he frankly forgave them both. Tell me, therefore, which of these two old boys will love him the most?"

And Simmy saith unto him, "The one whom he forgave most."

And Bossy said, "Thou hast judged rightly." And turneth to the weirdo from down Jermyn Street and saith unto Simmy, "Seest thou this woman? I entered into thy Club, but body lotion for my body didst thou not give me, nor designer uppers for my bipolar disorder; but she hath never ceased to render unto me her aromatherapy and to minister unto my feet, and hence my whole being holistically, with her reflexology. Wherefore I say unto thee, her alternative therapy and even her new-ageiness hath made her a qualified practitioner. And her former loopiness (which was in any the wise but a little loopiness) is no loopiness unto me."

And he turneth to the woman and saith, "Thy caring in the community hath made thee socially-included, and thy touchy-feeliness qualifieth thee for the Princess Di Medal for Sentimentality."

But the men in grey suits that sat at meat with him (for as it was written aforetime, the fish wast "off") wondered within themselves and said, "Who is this that excuseth the loopiness and doth make even them that are off their very trolleys to be socially-included?"

And, behold, he departed out of the *Carlton Club* and the household that was filled with boys (and girls) wearing the old school tie, and goeth out down the Old Kent Road.

Chapter Eleven

In which BOSSY breaks the garlic bread

nd when he was come into the country round about the Isle of Sheppey, for there was a rock festival on there, the multitudes pressed upon him for to hear his presentation and his counselling and to marvel at his wondrous narrative and spin. And they said within themselves, "Behold, he spins with authority."

The whole throng came upon him and he lift up his eyes and saith to Phil, "Whence shall we buy *ciabatta, formaggio* and *guacamole* that these may eat?" (And this he said to prove him, for he himself knew what he would do.)

And Phil said, "Verily there be not sufficient Eyetie nosh - no, not in all Islington never mind down here in the sticks - to feed this lot."

One of the groupies, Andy, Sim's brother (which was called Pete), saith unto him, "There's a lad here which hath a small basket of garlic bread - like unto that which is on the starter menu in *Carluccio's* - and two sardines; but what are they among so many?"

Bossy saith, "Be the sardines in olive oil or brine?"

Andy answereth and saith, "Nay, Administrator, but they be in tomato sauce."

Bossy saith, "Wondrous - for verily the tomato sauce is my fave! Make the multitude sit down."

Now there was much grass in the place, so they sat down, in number about five thousand, and smoked it.

And Matty the VAT man saith, "Not a bad turnout, Guv - but not as many as came to the *Rolling Stones*. And, behold, the *Stones* fans were not anhungered for they were all on that which is called 'charlie' and even on the 'E' which do turn off the anhungeredness, man."

And Bossy took the small basket of garlic bread and the five sardines in tomato sauce and, when he had raised his eyes and uttered something mawkish and fanciful concerning Fair Trade and Debt Relief, distributed the small basket of garlic bread and the two sardines to the groupies, and the groupies to them that were set down.

And they all did eat and were filled. And lo, his

"YES, OUR POVERTY AWARENESS SEMINARS COST £500 PER DAY"

groupies say amongst themselves, "How'd he do that, then?"

And Bossy did hear the words which the groupies spake concerning the apparently miraculous nosh, and he saith, "Although it wasn't a miracle in the way that old-fashioned, primitive and out-of-date religious cranks use the word 'miracle', it was an even greater miracle in the way. For Tom here knoweth of a decent boozer down in Eastchurch that does a mean garlic bread and could knock it out fast enough. Anywise, if people in the rich countries of the West will support political parties that have a global policy of foreign aid, then the underprivileged people in Africa and many other such places will be fed and live happy lives under the dictatorships which this Western money subsidiseth."

And when they heard these words, they were all amazed, and Andy turneth to Pete and saith, "If thou wilt believe that, then thou wilt believe anything!"

But Pete answereth, "I didn't understand a frigging word of it. English as a foreign language, if you ask me."

But Bossy turneth unto him and rebuketh him saying, "Verily it be not the English as a foreign language, but the language of Cloud Cuckoo Land."

Jim saith, "Shall we gather up the fragments, that nothing be lost?"

But John saith, "Nay - but leave the place like unto a rubbish tip as the custom be after these gigs. Hast thou not read what the Guru saith: 'The days shall come when many shall utter compassion for that which is called the environment; Nevertheless, they shall leave every place wherein they enter like unto a rubbish tip; And some other mugs will have to clear it up.'"

And Bossy saith unto Jon, "Thou hast well spoken."

Then the multitudes, when they had seen the modern "miracle" of debt relief and foreign aid - not the primitive religious twaddle which wast aforetime - said, "Verily this is that Moderniser that should come into the world!" And they departeth. And Hack did walk down unto Eastchurch, even unto the pub there.

And when Bossy and the groupies come away from

that island of Sheppey, they came again unto Islington. And, behold, there came Percy, he that was in the senior management team at the Beeb, which besought Bossy that he would come unto his apartment, for he saith, "My daughter hath the Attention Deficit Hyperactivity Disorder (ADHD). This group of disorders is characterised by: early onset; a combination of overactive, poorly modulated behaviour with marked inattention and lack of persistent task involvement; and pervasiveness over situations and persistence over time of these behavioural characteristics.

"It is widely thought that constitutional abnormalities play a crucial role in the genesis of these disorders, but knowledge on specific aetiology is lacking at present. In recent years the use of the diagnostic term 'Attention Deficit Disorder' for these syndromes has been promoted, though it implies a knowledge of psychological processes that is not yet available, and it suggests the inclusion of anxious, preoccupied, or 'dreamy' apethic subjects whose problems display alternative aetiologies. However, it is clear that, from the point of view of behaviour, problems of inattention constitute a central feature of these hyperkinetic syndromes.

"Secondary complications include dissocial behaviour and low self-esteem. There is, accordingly, considerable overlap between hyperkinesis and other patterns of disruptive behaviour, such as 'Unsocialised Conduct Disorder' (UCD) and 'Perverse Ratiocination and Trouble-causing' (PRAT)."

Bossy slept.

But he that was a member of the senior management team at the Beeb besought him in a loud voice, saying, "Moreover Fogey who broadcasts on the other side does say that she hath not the Attention Deficit Hyperactivity Disorder Syndrome, for that be a vain thing fondly invented and that verily there be no Attention Deficit Hyperactivity Disorder Syndrome. And besides all these things, today is *Attention Deficit Hyperactivity Disorder Day.*"

And Bossy had mercy on Percy and said, "What then does Fogey say concerning thy daughter?"

He answereth, "That she is a naughty little cow and needeth a bloody good hiding."

Now, for that it was Attention Deficit Hyperactivity Disorder Syndrome Day, there was much People in place and they watched him to see what he would do. For she hath the PRAT disease entered where they were sitting and cast herself down before them and made a great tumult so that the people were sore afraid.

And Bossy looketh upon her and saith, "Behold, she needeth not the bloody good hiding as Fogey does vainly believe, but the Cognitive Therapy and that which is called 'Positive Reinforcement'."

And she that hath the PRAT crieth out, "Piss off, wilt thou! They've tried all that psychology crap and I'll still do as I sodding well like. Gimme another Big Mac!"

Then her father, sorrowing, saith unto the PRAT, "Verily thou hast consumed this day even unto six of that which is called 'Big Mac'. Thinkest thou not, darling, that thou hast consumed sufficient unto the day?"

But she crieth out the more and saith, "Just piss off - and make this Bossy boots piss off with thee!"

And Bossy arose and took her by the hand and saith, "We'd better give her some *methylphenidate* or *dexamfetamine*, then - or it happeneth thou hast some *atomoxetine* in thy bathroom cabinet?"

But the PRAT did spit and saith unto him, "Get thy hands off me, thou dirty old sod! What - art thou a sodding paedophile, then?"

And Percy saith, "It doth not avail to give unto her the medicines, for verily she doth throw them up. For she hath the *bulimia* also." And he began to be exceeding sorrowful.

Then Bossy arose and said "Then Percy my boy you are right lumbered. But feareth thee not for thou shouldst get down to the Centre for Political Correctness in Romford - the same that is staffed by babes with obvious charms - wherein thou canst take a course in understanding the emotional needs of others in a politically correct way that does not discriminate against those with ADHD, nor against those that are naughty little cows, and then thou wilt be able to stand the constant tantrums. Also shall ye take the Poverty Awareness Course and the Climate Change Awareness Course and sundry other courses as shall be prescribed to thee. Oh and take thy credit card for thou wilt need it."

Chapter Twelve

In which BOSSY supports the SOCIAL WORKERS

And he cometh again into Southend and unto the offices of the Services which are called "Social" therein. And, behold, many of them that laboured in the Services which are called "Social" were compelled to be delivered of the Officer unto the Magistrate and from the Magistrate unto the Judge and from the Judge thence unto the whole Committee of Enquiry, for that they had suffered the little children to be offended and scourged by the old man who ran the care home; and they had not removed them from the care home of the man which did scourge and offend them.

And Bossy saith unto the Officer, "Wherefore compellest thou these our Social Workers to be delivered unto the Magistrate and from the Magistrate unto the Judge and from the Judge thence unto the whole Committee of Enquiry? What evil have they done?"

The Officer saith unto him, "For that they did not remove the little ones which are scourged and offended out of the hands of care home where they were scourged and offended."

But he was wroth and layeth hands suddenly on the Officer and saith, "Hast thou not heard how it is written in all the scrolls of that which is Standard Practice, that verily they that are the Social Workers err not, neither is any fault to be found in them whatsoever?"

And lo, the Officer was much discomfited and he saith, "But Facilitator, the little ones are grievously tormented and the marks of their torment appear in their flesh so that they sit not down, nor even lie on their beds, for the sore agony that doth torment them. And besides all these things, there were passeth the whole year in the which the Social Workers did write down all that came to pass concerning the little ones in their Case Histories. Yet do they not deliver them from the hands of the man which did evil. For this cause are they delivered unto the Magistrate and from the Magistrate unto the Judge and from the Judge thence unto the whole Committee of Enquiry."

But Bossy lift up his eyes and gazed steadfastly into Cloud Cuckoo Land and commanded that the Social Workers be set free, saying, "Whoso scourge and offend these little ones likewise. But whoso speaketh ill against any of these our Social Workers, it were better for him or her that he or she were socially excluded and cast into the depths of the Council Black list from whence neither she or he nor any of their dependent relatives be any more considered for re-housing on a nicer part of the sink estate."

And so, after that he had decreed a record of these events be indented into their very Career Dossiers and commanded that from henceforth they be monitored, the Magistrate let them go their way.

And straightaway they did return unto the Officer

that had (as they say in their language) "shopped" them and did make at that place a solemn vow: "We'll get the bastard. Nobody pisses about with us!"

And Bossy returned unto Romford and his groupies were with him.

And he began to say unto them in his doctrine, "It was said aforetime that ye are the salt of the earth. But I say unto you, take thee no more salt, for it raiseth thy blood pressure and it may be that ye crumple with an heart attack or, as it might be, a stroke."

And they marvelled that the Latest Thing had given such wisdom unto men. Then drew near an old boy in tweeds for to hear him. And he said to the groupies, "This man receiveth oiks and yobbos and them that are called 'vulnerable' and 'disadvantaged persons from the inner city' and 'differently abled' People and them that do have 'alternative lifestyles'; also the 'multicultural'."

But his groupies rebuked them, saying, "OK. OK We haven't time for the whole list!"

And Bossy, turning to the old boy in tweeds, saith unto him, "Which of you having an hundred sheep, if he or she loseth one of them on the Sabbath day, doth not leave the ninety-nine, go to the pub and catch the Eurostar first thing Monday morning to put in his or her missing livestock claim under the terms of the Common Agricultural Policy?"

"And when he or she receiveth the compensation to which he or she is entitled, he or she putteth the cash in his or her pocket and rejoiceth. And when he or she cometh home, he or she saith unto his or her colleagues, 'Lets go get pissed. It's my round. For, behold, I do screw the taxpayer this umpteenth time!'

And the old boy durst not answer him a word - for he had no sheep and moreover disliked the European Union.

And he saith, "Behold, it is not the Politically-Correct which require re-education and consciousness-raising so that they be aware of the special needs of minorities, but the reconstructed reactionaries and old farts, like unto you."

Then the old boy saith, "Facilitator, we know that thou hast been on all the appropriate training courses and that thou hast skills more than any man can number. Tell us, therefore, what will become of transgressors at the last?

"For Moses gave us a Law and the prophets, and by this Law they that do sin shall perish and they that are righteous shall receive everlasting life. And Jesus hath said that the righteous shall have everlasting inheritance but the sinners shall depart unto everlasting fire. Tell us, therefore, what dost thou say?"

And Bossy looked on them, sorrowing, and saith, "O fools and slow of heart to believe all that the prophets did tell thee! For Moses indeed gaveth the Law, and Jesus hath said that they which are sinners shall depart into everlasting fire. "But I say unto you, ye shall not be judgmental in anything. For Moses and the prophets and Jesus spake unto the people as the People understanded in the old time. But in the Great Modernisation, behold, the former things are done away. And lo, in modern times there is no sin, neither is there guiltiness - for guiltiness doth take away thy self-esteem; and it is a grievous thing to lose one's self-esteem.

"There be, therefore, no sin nor wrongdoing. For hearken thou unto my saying that in these times which are called 'progressive' and 'emancipated', there is only that which is called 'lifestyle'. And everyone can do as he or she sodding well likes - except that which be politically-inncorrect.

"For all manner of what was formerly sin, and all manner of iniquity, shall be forgiven thee - except the sin of political-incorrectness for the which there is no forgiveness only endless persecution and hatred."

When he heard this saying, the old boy departed sorrowing - for he was very politically-incorrect.

Then Bossy saith unto his groupies, "Behold, there was a certain fat cat which was clothed in ***Armani*** and fine ***Calvin Kleins*** and which did nosh sumptuously every day at *Cafe de la Comment est Votre Pere?* And there was a certain underprivileged person named Laz, which was receipt of benefits, laid at his gate full of psychosomatic skin disorders, and desiring to be filled with the leftovers from the promos that the fat cat splasheth out on for the hangers on in his media empire.

"Moreover the paparazzi came and did photograph him for the photo-shoot which appeareth on the TV news for the fulfillment of the mawkishness of the People which do love to behold that which doth resemble picturesque poverty.

"And it came to pass that Laz's benefits were greatly increased and, behold, he findeth it among his substance to install the digital telly, the cool new Playstation for his sprogs and the chav jewellery for his slag.

"But the fat cat was indicted under section two, subsection 39 of the Companies Act and cast into prison. And in prison he lift up his eyes and said, 'O thou Minister for Equal Opportunities, have mercy on me and send Laz that he may photocopy his latest fraudulent appeal to Benefits Office, that I might send it under mine own name and partake of the handouts thereof.'

"But the Minister of Equal Opportunities saith, 'Son, remember that thou in thy fatcatness received thy megalifestyle, and likewise Laz only that state benefits whereby he benefiteth - and whatsoever other he did accordingly scam. Now he hath his benefits increased and thou hast been nobbled. And beside all this, between Laz and thyself social discrimination on the basis of class and economic determinism is fixed, so that they which would pass from the scrounger to the supernannuated fatcats cannot pass; neither they which are among the bloated plutocrats may pass to the bloody oiks.'

"Then he said, 'I pray thee, Minister for Equal Opportunites, that thou wouldst send Laz to my ex's house, for we have the five sprogs which are also into the wheeler-dealing (and verily thou knowest how it is when thou seekest to make a bob or two on the side - know what I mean?), and tip them off also as to when they are nigh unto being fingered.'

"But the Minister for Equal Opportunities saith, 'They know the usual crooks within the Financial Services Sector - let them hear them.'

"But he saith, 'Nay Mr Minister, but if one of the insider dealers went unto them, they would watch their backs.'

"But the Minister answered and said, 'Behold, if they hear not the usual crooks within the Financial

Services Sector, neither will they be persuaded though on should go unto them from the insider dealer.'"

And the groupies did marvel at his words. But Magda she marvelled not, but did sneak Bossy away unto a private place. And there they did look at the books and did discuss the business of the Centre. And Magda did say "Behold the bookings from ladies of a certain age are always up when thou art in Romford and do preach at the Centre thyself. Verily I think they do fancy the pants off you. Best keep our cosy shack up a secret."

"In truth this is so," saith Bossy.

"And lo," continueth Magda. "We had to get rid of that Tracey from the front desk, the one that Andy hath been knocking off, for she hath gone all prim and proper and refuseth to flash her knockers at the male guests. That Chardonnay hath taken her place, and she weareth a halter-neck of

wondrous lowness to the joy of our male customers and the benefit of our cash flow."

And thus they spake of other secret things.

Chapter Thirteen

In which BOSSY cureth a man of POLITICAL INCORRECTNESS

nd Bossy spake a spin unto his groupies to this end, that People ought always to demand their rights and complain, and never get sick of complaining.

"There was in a city a certain Council Official which was no fan of the Latest Thing and pretty much a bastard to boot. And there was an old biddy in that city, and she came to him, saying 'Avenge me of mine adversary. It's those pillocks at No.84. She has men up and down her stairs till all hours and he's never anywhere to be seen. It happeneth he hath done a runner - and frankly, one look at her and I don't blame him. (But that's beside the point.) The little sods ride their motorbikes on the pavement; and their cats do foul on my strawberries.'

"And the Council Official, for that he was a Council Official, doeth nothing about it. But the old biddy was diligent in her complaining and in the demand for her rights withal. And, behold, she writeth letters in the green ink whereof the Official comprehendeth not, for the old biddy had aforetime been at the Bog Standard Comprehensive and therefore she knew not her letters nor even how to write them.

"Moreover, she cometh and standeth beneath the window of the Council Office and maketh a great disturbance, so that the whole Council and they that sat about idle by day and by night in the offices cried out and said unto the Official, 'Can't you get rid of this toe rag which is pestilential by day and by night with her "frigging this" and her "frigging that"?'

"And he would not for a while. But afterward he said within himself, 'Though I have no love for the oiks and the yobbos, and though I dwell in a great house in a nice part of town and not on that Council Estate dump, I am become wearied of her complaining and her jealousy for her right.

"'I am purposed therefore to avenge her. Not for that her strawberries, behold, they are covered in cat pooh, nor for that her neighbour runneth a knocking shop right next door, nor yet for that her sprogs (which verily be pillocks) do ride their motorbikes on the pavement; but for that she hath complied with full compliance with all the statutes and ordinances that must be complied with under the rules governing Compliance and that she hath fulfilled the requirements of that which is called Health and Safety and the responsibilities of council tenants under the Council Tenants Act, being the Act for the pursuance of all matters which have aught to do with tenants and the aforementioned Council.

"'And besides, she pisseth me off with her freaking whingeing. For a contentious woman and a ceaseless dropping on a very rainy day, are not they like unto each other?'"

When Bossy had left off his speaking, his groupies say unto him, "Facilitator, we know that thou art a compliant person and Politically-Correct in all that thou dost teach, tell us the meaning of this spin, for we cannot tell what it doth mean."

And he saith, "God - you are thick! It just means that if you shower a guy with enough paperwork and bore his backside off with complaining, you'll get what you want in the end!"

But they comprehended not this saying and, behold, it was hid from their eyes.

And he spake this spin unto certain that trusted in themselves that they were totally compliant and despised others: "Behold, a Politically-Correct person and an old fart went on a chat show on *TV*. And the old fart saith, I'm not PC at all. I think it's a totalitarianism-lite. It's a way of stifling free speech. It's a denial of English political history and the historic settlements which always guaranteed healthy discussion and disagreement."

"And the studio audience laughed him to scorn.

"But the Politically-Correct person, when the fawning Quiz Master bade her come unto the microphone, saith, 'Behold, I contribute to every tsunami relief going and ever on *Princess Di Day* do throw my teddy bears and weep these many buckets. I patronise everybody on the scale of equality, regardless of race, gender or religious orientation. And lo, when it cometh to *Red Nose Day*, I do put on my red nose which is exceedingly red.'

"I say unto you that this PC person is of a truth more cool and loveth the Latest Thing more than the old fart which shall be cast into outer darkness and not allowed to come on telly a second time."

And when they heard these things, behold, they marvelled that the Latest Thing had given such expertise unto persons.

At about this time Bossy passed by on his way to Romford Station from the Centre for Political Correctness, yea for he had a TV crew following him that day to filmeth "A Day in the Life of a Modern Guru" for Percy at the Beeb. There he saw a man that was partially-sighted from birth. And his groupies said unto him, "Facilitator, who was politically-incorrect, this man or his parents that he was born partially-sighted?

For happeneth it not that sexism and racism are handed down through the genes even unto the third and fourth generations of them that be politically-incorrect?"

Bossy saith, "Both this man and his parents were politically-incorrect - and this bugger still is!"

And, behold, he that was partially-sighted began to cry out in a loud voice so many words which were politically-incorrect that no man could number them. For it happeneth that a differently-abled person came that way, and, behold, the politically-incorrect man crieth, "I can see you - you cripple!"

And whosoever passed by that way he did cry after in his political-incorrectness: "Fatso!" and "God she's ugly - what a sight!" and even "Coon!" Moreover, the politically-incorrect man wore a coat of fur and smoketh the *Gauloises*.

When he saw Bossy he cried out the more, "Ah, so it's you, Facilitator, Moderniser General! What have I to do with thee? Hast thou come to torment me?"

But Bossy, when he drew near, had pity on him and bade him be silent. And he was silent, and the People watched him to see what he would do. And Bossy took from his scrip a pair of the coolest contact lenses from *Specsavers*, laid them on him that was politically-incorrect and partially-sighted.

And he saith, "Take thou these *Euphemismia* lenses and be thou healed of thy partially-sightedness, and it happeneth also that, seeing, thou mayest be delivered of thy political-incorrectness."

And straightaway he that was partially-sighted saw clearly and he saith no more "Fatso!" but "Ooh look - there's a beautiful and generously proportioned person!" and "What a nice young man from an ethnic minority!"

And the People marvelled that such miracles were done among them. But an old fart who was near did saith, "This be not he that was politically-incorrect - for no man maketh the politically-incorrect to be Politically-Correct."

And Bossy, when he heard these things, was wroth and saith, "This sign is for the hardness of your heart, for verily it is sign of the Latest Thing."

And for their hardness of heart, he turneth to him that was aforetime politically-incorrect and saith unto him, "Say ye that this old fart is a bastard?"

And he saith, "Nay Facilitator, for that had been my custom in the days of my politically-incorrectness. But now I say no more that he is a bastard but a socially-excluded person which requireth inclusion, compassion and caring."

And Bossy saith unto him, "Thou hast well said. Sayest

thou also that he has need of counselling?"

And he answereth, "Yea, Facilitator, for all have need of the counselling and of the re-education, awareness-training, consciousness-raising and therapy of every kind. Such counselling as I believe is provided at a centre in Romford, verily one staffed by young ladies of obvious charms. "

And the People marvelled and said among themselves, "Behold, now we know for a surety that he is verily the Latest Thing on Earth, for he maketh both the partially-sighted to see and the politically-incorrect to receive of their correctness."

And he that had been partially-sighted and politically incorrect did arise and make his way unto the nearest pub where Magda did give him the promised monkey, yea even in crisp tenners.

In which BOSSY mocks the KIPPERS

nd Bossy draweth night unto Camden and, behold, Crispin the Five-Fruit-and-Vegetables Enforcer was there. But the press of the People was very great and Crispin crieth the cry of his enforcement in vain over the noise of the multitude.

And, behold, there was a man named Zacky, which was chief among the old farts whom his kinsfolk and acquaintance called the Grand Old Buffer. And Zacky was desirous of seeing Bossy, but could not for that he was vertically-challenged. He ran, therefore, and climbed up a lamp-post to see him, for he was to pass that way.

And Zacky was exceeding rich for that he doth have a factory in the cigarette manufacture, so he was known among men as Zacky-Tabacy. And when Bossy was come unto that place he looked up and saw him and saith, "Zacky, make haste and come down, for I must dine with thee this day!"

Therefore Zacky did grin and shimmy down the lamp-post like unto smartish, like.

And they came unto Crispin and gave him two quid and he rendered unto them ten pieces of fresh fruit and singeth to them a couple of verses of the jingle which wast commanded of the Healthy Eating Commissar.

But the People which was exceeding health-conscious and bumclenchingly Politically-Correct, when they saw it they murmured and said, "This man eateth with Zacky-Tabaccy which is an outcast of the People for that he maketh the cancer sticks."

And Zacky, knowing what was in their hearts, saith unto Bossy, "For thy sake I repent of my cigarette manufacture and hereby sell all my tobacco shares and donate the money to the Lesbian and Gay Christian Movement, for the gay knocking shop which knocketh there in the very crypt and for the after-civil-partnerships piss-up."

When he heard these words, Bossy saith, "This day shalt thou have four score Brownie points."

And all the People cried out, "Brill! Nicotine patches all round!"

Then cometh Bossy unto the City and taketh his seat among the bankers. And lo, there were they which are called "Europhiles" there, having their snouts in the trough of the Euro Bail Out Fund. And without were old boys of the Kipper Party, which are them that hate the EU for they are taxed to payeth for the Euro Bail Out Fund. And the people watched him to see what he would do receiving physicians of that which is called "spin" from the household of the Prime Bureaucrat that they might entangle him in his talk. And they say unto him, "Facilitator, we know that thou art a lover of the Latest Thing and thou art Politically-Correct in all things; tell us therefore, is it lawful to argue for the EU budget rebate or no?" And this they said, tempting him, for they knew that the place was absolutely teeming with old boys of the Kipper Party, which are them that hate the EU.

But he, percieving their craftiness, saith, "Why tempt ye me? Shew me a Euro." And they shew it. And he saith, "Whose image and superscription hath it?"

And one crieth, "They're all different! But this one hath something that looketh like a frigging gorilla."

So Bossy said "Render the coin with the frigging gorilla unto the frigging gorilla."

And the physicians of that which is called "spin" departed, for they could not answer him a word to this saying. And the rumour of him spread abroad so that the Kippers said, rejoicing, "Seest thou how he screwed the Europhiles!"

And some said, "Verily he hath not screwed the Europhiles, but did turn against the Kippers." And their witnesses agreed not together.

And so Bossy sendeth an email unto Sebastian who did visit the EU Embassy about the coin with the gorilla. And the EU Embassy, the same that is within Smith Square unto Westminster, did send grants and subsidies unto the Centre in Romford, the same that is staffed by young ladies of obvious charms. And Bossy did henceforth speak wisely of the Euro and the Working Time Directive and the Bail Out Funds - declaring them all to be Politically Correct and beloved of all nice folk. And Percy of the Beeb had him on Panorama to explain how the survival of the Euro was for the good of all and was worth every penny of the taxes. And Bossy saith "Behold we are enlightened internationalists who do love the European Union, while those who do warn of economic collapse are but xenophobic little englanders, and racists to boot".

And there was a wailing and a gnashing of teeth among the Kippers. And Hack did put in a Freedom of Information request in Brussels.

And, behold, Bossy and his groupies departed that region and came unto Hampstead Heath and dwelt among the gays there which cease not their groping and casual assignations in the daytime nor in the night-season also.

And he saith, "I say unto you that a man shall leave his wife and shall cleave unto his brother, and there shall be the great multitude of alternative lifestyles and sexual preferences; for this is the doing of the Latest Thing."

But Andy saith unto him, "Facilitator, be there they which join not themselves unto the company of the gay, nor to them which are called 'Lipstick Lesbians' or of the Dungarees Party?"

And he answereth and saith, "Yea, Andy, thou hast well spoken. There yet be those which *know* one another in the biblical sense. And these shall screw around, for this also is of that which is lifestyle."

But he saith, "Ah, Facilitator, but what shall a woman do if, after that she hath screwed around greatly according to thy word, she discovereth she be with child?"

And he saith, "As it is written, she shall go to the abortionist and verily he shall rip that which is within her untimely from her womb."

But Andy saith, "How shall these things be? For this is a hard saying, Facilitator. I know that thou art the Moderniser General and that it be a liberated thing for men and women to screw around; but it happeneth that there are so many which be with child, even a great multitude so that no man can number them. Is it lawful for them all, every woman, to get herself to the abortionist and for that which is within her to ripped untimely from her womb? How can this be?"

And he saith, "It happeneth in the aforetime, when the days were evil, that after a woman had screwed around - as it is written in their language, 'and had her fun' - behold, she was compelled to deliver that which was within her; and, her lifestyle wast buggered up no end.

"But in the days of our Progress, when the Modernisation is come and the miracles of the modern science are available to all without discrimination and free on the NHS - then this that is called 'untimely ripped', what is it but the modern form of that which was aforetime called 'contraception'?"

Andy saith "But, behold, Facilitator, they have already the contraceptive, that which is called 'the Pill'. For a surety, it doth not weigh heavily on a woman to take unto herself the Pill before she goeth forth on the razzle?"

But he was wroth and his countenance was darkened and he spake unto Andy, saying, " The modern woman shall not be discomfited by that they should remember to take the Pill. Behold, oftimes it be not expedient for them to remember it. And they shall in no wise bear the burden of remembering it; for that were to interfere with their lifestyle."

"But the children, Facilitator, they that are untimely ripped - what sayest thou concerning them?"

And he saith, "Suffer the little children."

And he took unto himself his groupies and began to speak of himself, how he would be delivered into the hands of Fogey and sundry old farts and that he would be mocked and satirised wickedly; but after three days he would make a comeback.

In which BOSSY cleanses THE BEEB

nd when they drew nigh unto the Great City, and were come to the mount that is called Primrose Hill, Bossy sent two of his groupies, saying unto them, "Go into those streets over against you and ye shall find a bicycle tied to a lamp-post there, and another bicycle (actually a slightly older model) with it. Loose them and bring them unto me. And if any man say aught unto you, ye shall say, 'The Facilitator hath need of them'."

All this was done that it might be fulfilled which is spoken of the Facilitator by the Green Guru, saying, "Tell them all in the Great City, behold, thy Moderniser General cometh unto thee, Green and riding a bike; and with a slightly older model of a bike."

And the groupies went and did as Bossy commanded them, and brought the new bike and the old bike (with the regulation *Day-Glo* waterproofs and the crash helmets, according as it is written in the section three (Attire) of the Regulations for Cyclists). And Bossy sat thereon and did enter even into the Great City.

And a very great multitude threw their teddy bears in the way, and others cast floral tributes in his path and cried, saying, "Cheers to the Moderniser General! Cool is he that cometh in the name of the Latest Thing! Cheers all round, mate!"

And when he was come into the City, the whole place was, like, euphoric and freaked out, saying, "This is Bossy, the Guru from Southend, the Tsar for Political-Correctness and the Moderniser General."

And Bossy entered into Broadcasting House and cast out all them that made elitist programmes and which did the "talking heads" documentaries which were in the old time. And he over threw the laptops of them that brought forth the classical concerts and produced serious talks.

And he saith unto them, "It is written, Broadcasting House shall be an house of noisy soundtracks and whirling captions, but ye have made it a den of elitism!"

And the partially-sighted and they that complaineth of all manner of fashionable neuroses came unto him; and he did counsel them all and send them with the alternative medicines even off to Romford with their credit cards.

And, behold, he spake even unto the children that were obese, and said, "Get ye off the chicken nuggets and take unto yourselves the cabbage and cucumber!"

And all the children with one voice said, "Yuk!"

And when the old broadcasters saw the modern and progressive things that he did, and the children - even also them that were obese - doing their ethnic dancing in honour of him so that all their parents cooed and simpered and made the noise that is, in their language, written "Aaah!", they were sore displeased.

And all the unreconstructed reactionaries and conservatives said, "See ye not these things and hear ye not what things they cry out? It's not decent. Even the fatsos are doing it."

But he answered and said, "Yea, have ye never heard how it was written 'Out of the mouths of babes and suckling fatso shall proceed hysterical ecstasies'?"

And Percy of the Beeb was raised up unto the highest seat. And he declareth a new rule saying "Blessed are the tolerant and the multicultural. And we shall respect all views and all opinions, excepting those that are Politically Incorrect, or opposeth the EU or opposeth wind farms or sayeth that capitalism is a good idea or that supporteth cutting taxes or any who otherwise blaspheme against the teachings of Bossy and of Political Correctness. Yea, all those will be trodden underfoot, sacked and banned from the airwaves. Thus will we enter a new dawn of tolerance and understanding for all." And all the new broadcasters did cheer him. And all the old broadcasters were cast out and behold they createth a desolation and called it tolerance.

And when Bossy was leaving out of Broadcasting House, the old broadcasters, yea those who were not unemployed, enquired of him, saying, "Tell us by what authorisation is thy facilitating facilitated, O Facilitator? And according to which sections of the Standard Practice art thou standardised?"

But Bossy answered them, and said, "I will go ask of you one thing, which if you tell me, I shall in like a manner tell you by what authorisation mine own authority be authorised. "For consider, the aquatherapy of Jak the Aquatherapist, whence was it - from the old farts or the Latest Thing?"

And they therefore answered Bossy, and said, "We cannot tell."

Then he saith, "Neither tell I you by what authorisation my authority be authorised."

And he spake unto them in spins, saying, "Did ye never read the Treaties which be from Rome and Maastricht and even Amsterdam, how the nation shall be removed from your authority according to the Constitution by which it is constituted? Therefore, I say unto you that when the European Superstate doth come,

then your kingdom shall no more be your kingdom and your authority no more your authority. For the former things are passed away, according as it is written in the Constitution."

And, behold, they could not answer him unto any of these things.

Then did Bossy go unto the Palace that is Westminster and did speak unto the men in grey suits saying "Behold the Prime Bureaucrat who Knows Not What He Does is Politically Incorrect, which is the greatest sin in mine eyes. Have I not made Percy of the Beeb the chief of the Beeb? Will he not mock the Politically Incorrect, even unto all the news and current affairs programmes that will be broadcast from now until the General Election?"

And the men in grey suits did mutter among themselves saying "He that is mocked of the Beeb cannot win an election. We need a new Prime Bureaucrat who can win the election, and moreover save us our seats in Parliament that we continue to have our snouts in the trough and employ our totty as secretaries while the wives are at home in the constitiuency all unknowing." And they turneth to Bossy and asketh "Who shall we appoint in the place of the Prime Bureaucrat who Knows Not What He Does?"

And Bossy did not answer them directly. "I am not sent to dictate to you, but only to minister unto you and guide you to the paths of righteousness." And he left them. But on the table he left behind a copy of the Guardian in which was an article naming one of them as "a right-on dude". So the men in grey suits did look unto the right on dude with favour. They did cast down the Prime Bureaucrat who Knows Not What He Does and in his place did put the Prime Bureaucrat who is Right On.

And Bossy again spake unto them in his spin, and said, "The EU Superstate is like unto a certain Commissioner (not Man-Del-Son) which made a civil partnership ceremony for his son, and sent forth his officials to call them that were issued with freebies to come to the civil partnership ceremony; and they would come.

"And again he sent forth his servants, saying, 'The French lamb and rocket salad are prepared, the disco is booked and the lines of charlie are laid out in the loos. Come, for all is now ready.'

"But they made light of it, for they said within themselves, 'Verily we have had a better offer.'

"And the remnant took his officials and mocked them concerning the rocket salad and the shameless promos for all things Frog; and they did debag them and paint their very backsides with the blue paint.

"And when the Commissioner heard thereof, he went ballistic and commanded his officials, saying, 'Slap ASBOs on the whole damn lot!'

"And they slappeth the ASBOs on them.

"Then saith the Commissioner, 'The civil partnership ceremony is now ready, but they that were bidden were a bunch of twats. Go forth into the sink estates unto all them that are vulnerable and socially-excluded and which lacketh the table manners and bring them in.'

"So those officials went forth as he had commanded them and brought in all the oiks and yobbos and, behold, the civil partnership ceremony was furnished with guests which had not the table manners and stuffed themselves like there was no tomorrow.

"And when the Commissioner came in to see the guests, he saith, 'Bloody hell - where'd you find this sodding lot? I've gotta find some way of getting this swinish multitude off the premises. I am purposed what I shall do.'

"And he seeth a man there which was an illegal immigrant and saith unto him, 'How camest thou in here without a work permit?'

"But he was gobsmacked and saith, 'I wist not that I must needs furnish myself with the aforesaid work permit. I thought this was a piss-up.'

"And the Commissioner saith, 'Tag the bastard and chuck him out! For, behold, it is written in the European Constitution that care must be provided for the disadvantaged, the vulnerable, the under priviledged and the socially-excluded - but not in the palaces of the Commissioners, neither within many kilometers of their palaces.'"

Then did Bossy speak likewise unto the men of the opposition regarding their leader. And they too did cast down their leader, and they did raise in his place Helen who was so politically correct it maketh thine eyes water, and who was a black, one-legged lesbian to boot.

And Bossy left them and went out across the City unto Tower Hamlets and lodged there, for he saith, "The days are come when all shall be modernised, irrespective of race, creed, colour, gender, sexual orientation or disability."

And they marvelled, and said, "How shall these things be, seeing that there be many which like not the modernisation?"

And he saith, "Behold, the Prime Bureaucrat who is

Right On and the physicians of that which is called 'spin' shall compel them to be modernised. For with the Latest Thing all things are possible."

And in the morning, when he came again into the City, he was anhungered and seeth that the emporium which provideth the figs and the lentils, the sesame seeds and the aloe vera was closed - for they that had the emporium, behold, they had pissed off to the Live 8 concert. He therefore enquired of them, saying, "Why do they that sell the figs and the lentils, the sesame seeds and even the aloe vera piss off to the Live 8 concert?"

And they say unto him, "For their heart is set on rooting out utterly all hunger in Africa and making the whole world a nice place and everybody happy, irrespective of race, creed, sexual orientation or disability."

But he saith, "But I'm one of the hungry! The bastards should have started with me."

And he was wroth and saith unto all them that stood by, "Let this emporium be no more an emporium, neither let them sell the figs and the lentils, the sesame seeds and even the aloe vera."

And, behold, he closeth it down under section four, subsection three, paragraph seven of the Food and Hygiene (Premises) Act.

And they marvelled, saying, "Behold, who is like unto the Moderniser General? For lo, no one doeth such modernisation unless the Latest Thing be with him."

But he saith unto them, "Why marvel ye that I said unto thee that this emporium shall be no more an emporium, neither sell the figs and the lentils, the sesame seeds and even the aloe vera? If ye had the regulations for healthy eating, even so much as a grain of sesame seed, ye would say unto this pie shop, 'Be thou shut down!' - and, behold, it shutteth down straightaway; and unto this donut stall, 'Be thou no longer a donut stall!' and likewise it shall turn into a juice bar. And all things whatsoever ye do with compliance, continuous assessment and accountability shall be done unto you."

In which BOSSY speaketh of the GREAT MODERNISING to come

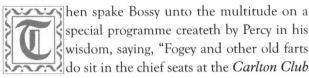hen spake Bossy unto the multitude on a special programme createth by Percy in his wisdom, saying, "Fogey and other old farts do sit in the chief seats at the *Carlton Club* and in many other clubs. And they clothe not themselves after the manner of the People - for they have neither the baseball cap nor the trainers. For they say, 'Verily we be not of the oiks, oikish; but put on the thick tweed suit or off-times the striped trousers.'

"They eat not of the five portions of fruit every day, as the Five-Fruit-and-Vegetables Enforcer commandeth them. For they say this be food which is for the wild coneys (as it is said in their tongue, 'rabbit food') and take for themselves that which is called in their language the 'spotted dick' and 'bread and butter' pudding. And verily they do smoke, and drink claret and go forth with the horses and hounds. All these abominations do they notwithstanding the continual importunings of propaganda from our State which is called 'Nanny'.

"Woe, therefore, unto Fogey and old farts which they do say that there be no Narcissistic Personality Disorder, only that men are selfish twats.

"Woe unto Fogey and the old farts which say that men do sin, when we do know, according to the gospel which was spoken unto us by the Guru Freud (which oft-times be written 'Fraud') that verily they are in the domination of that which is called 'Unconscious Motivation'.

"Woe unto Fogey and the old farts which be exceeding judgmental and do say that there be sin and that it be very Original, and standeth in the following of Adam. For verily we believe that the People are nice and good and getting better all the time - as that which they that are called the *Beatles* do sing.

"And that, lo, it was the old time which verily doeth evil, but now that the Modernisation is come, we do know how smart we are and need not all that old morality crap. And that, lo, all that is requireth is that every person be filled with self-esteem.

"For that it was once said, 'Thou shalt not commit adultery', I say unto thee, behold, thou art that which is called 'liberated'. Go forth and screw whatsoever thou likest, be thy man, woman or beast of the field - only see that thou wearest a condom.

"Woe unto those that say the little children shall be governed according unto all that is given in the tradition, what thou shalt learn thereby in wisdom and understanding. And instead do thou give thyself and thy children unto that which is called 'creativity' and 'self-expression' and let it all hang out.

"For, behold, it was written aforetime that thou shalt keep all the sayings of the Lord in thine heart to love them and to obey; but I say unto thee: Believe what the sod thou likest, for, behold, it is written in the Great Modernisation and of them that teach it, 'Everyone hath the right to his or her own opinion - the no matter how sodding gormless.'

"Therefore, if they say unto thee, 'Thou hast that which is true and good in the voice of the Scriptures and the worship of Him that is called The Lord', thou shalt say unto them, 'Be thou not so bloody elitist and chauvinistic. For verily we have also the Feng Shui and the Crystals and the Aromatherapy and all manner of that therapy which is called "Alternative"'.

"And if they shall say unto thee, 'Lo, here is the music which was sung unto us by our forefathers', do thou answer them and declare that thou wouldst rather the heavy metal and the grunge, for verily that which they do call 'headbanging', is it not equal unto that which is called Bach? And they that will not say shall be condemned elitist.

"And, behold, whosoever humbleth him or herself shall be judged lacking in self-esteem; but she or he that promoteth herself or himself shall become a celeb."

And Bossy went out and departed from the BBC and he was approached by the editors of the newspapers and the magazines and such other media as were won to the cause of Political Correctness. One did ask him to write about the dangers of Global Warming, another about the joys of the simple life and a third about the wonders of the European Union. And Bossy did retire unto his abode at Stapleford Abbotts where Magda helpeth him to write the articles to the amazement of all and sundry.

But when he came down unto the Great City to dine in justly deserved splendour with the editors, his groupies came unto him for to show him the great buildings which were built in the City in the old time. And Bossy saith unto them, "See ye all these buildings? Verily I say unto you there shall not be left one stone standing upon another that shall not be thrown down and replaced by modern structures which be the machines for the People to live in.

"And, behold, there shall be no likeness among them, so that here a needle skyscraper and there a gherkin; here a concrete block like unto them that were built at Nuremburg in the days of their enslavement and at that which is called in their language 'Lubyanka'; there behold one with its innards on the outside wherein the walls shall be painted black.

"For verily the Truth is greater than the facts."

But his groupies understood none of these things which he saith and, behold, their understanding was darkened and their eyes were closed concerning this saying. Then Bart saith unto him, "O Facilitator, we know for a surety that thou hast wisdom passing the wisdom of any person - even Solomon which did build the temple. Tell us, therefore, surely the City will appear, as it is said among infants and children, 'all higgledy-piggledy and that'.

And, behold, they that dwell in the place which hath its innards on the outside, that is all black within, verily they shall grow pissed off so that they top themselves for very pissed-offedness?"

But Bossy rebuked him, and said, "Behold, I have told thee before: thou must become utterly infantilised or thou shalt not see the Great Modernisation."

And as he sat on Primrose Hill and did look down on the City, the groupies say unto him, "Tell us when shall these things be, and when shall the Great Modernisation appear. What signs will there be?"

And he saith, "I say unto you, look not here for the Great Modernisation, or there. For the Modernisation is within you. And except ye be modernised in your heart, ye cannot enter in the New Project, neither into the infantilisation which is amongst you already, nor the Great Modernisation by which all shall be modernised.

"But take heed that none deceive you. For many shall come from the East End and from the West End shall say, 'I am the Great Moderniser and shall deceive many.

"But there shall be signs over the air and in the www. When ye see that the People do put on their red noses, then know ye for a surety that **Red Nose Day** draweth nigh. And when ye do behold how they paint their faces and camp themselves up all along the street that is called Piccadilly, then ye know also that *Gay Pride Day* cometh upon you.

"So likewise when ye see the former things, how they pass away, then know that the Great Modernisation is upon you. For in the old time it was said, 'We have Law of the Lord and by this shall all men be judged, whether they depart into everlasting life or into flames which die not.'

"But I say unto you that when the Spirit of Modernisation is come, there shall be no rewards and no punishment, for there shall be no law. There shall be neither what was called 'praise' or 'blame', but only Fame. And there shall be neither right nor wrong, but only that which is called 'Lifestyle'. For behold of anything, is it not as good as another thing?

"And in aforetime, they said, 'Give unto us the scrolls and the songs which were written by them that were reknowned for their greatness.' But in the days of your Modernisation, they shall no more read the old scrolls which were renowned for the good which they did bestow, nor shall your singers sing the old songs. For all these things shall be done away with and the People shall read glossy crap and their ears shall hear the music that doeth thine head in.

"In those days the children shall not be rebuked, neither learn they their letters. For I am the Way, the Truth and the Life. The Way, lo, it is any way that a person pleaseth, and it shall be said they have their right to go that way. And the Truth - behold, the Truth is that there be no Truth, but what everyone thinketh in his or her own thinking. And the Life, it shall be that wherein they shall proceed from one humourless abasement unto the next. And, behold, they shall all be pissed.

"But woe unto you, old farts, which do say that the Modernisation is a vain thing which gladdeneth not the heart of man. For this ye shall be called 'Elitist' and depart into everlasting gloom. And, behold, ye shall be marginalised. For the days shall come that there shall be no more 'elitism' but only that which is called 'accessibility'; neither 'classic' but what, if it be not 'pop' and 'rock' is crossover'. And if anyone shall say, 'Lo, this be a work of art, or that', then so it shall be."

And they asked him, "When shall these things be?"

And he saith, "Behold, there shall be earthquakes in divers places, the sea and the waves roaring - for Global Warming shall be over all the Earth.

"And when Political-Correctness is preached in all the whole world, then shall the Great Modernisation come."

Chapter Seventeen

In which BOSSY is BETRAYED

nd, behold, Bossy taketh aside his groupies, and saith, "The Narrative which I do spin is hid from they that are of old farts, that having eyes they see not and ears they hear not, lest they be converted and become Politically-Correct. But to you it is given to know the secrets of the spun Narrative, that, seeing, ye might become my apparatichiks and even be numbered among them that are my cronies.

"Ye that do ask for a sign, hear, therefore, the spun Narrative, and, hearing, understand. For then shall the Cloud Cuckoo Land be likened unto ten slappers which snorted their charlie and went unto the Feast of Glastonbury. And five of them were savvy and five were kooky. And they that were kooky were on the pull but took they no Pill with them. But the savvy, which were on the pull also, taketh them Pills plenteously.

"And lo, they begin all to screw themselves rotten until, at the last, they fell down, everyone pissed out of their heads and, like, totally shagged out. And it came to pass that, after many days, it ceased to be with the kooky after the manner of women and they were sore afraid, and they do cry one to another, 'Bugger me, Megan - or as it be Amber or Jessica - I'm up the duff!'

"But they that had been savvy, behold, they were not up the duff, neither were they knocked up or bumped. And, behold, they do go forth a second time and even unto the third and fourth times unto the rock concert and the disco and do shag themselves exceeding rotten. And, behold, they are neither bumped nor up the duff.

"So it shall be with everyone that is totally modernised, for in those days they shall fear not to shag whomsoever cometh upon them in the daytime and night-season."

But Pete saith unto him, "'Ere, but look. Them that got up the duff, they could just have an abortion, couldn't they? Get rid of it?"

And Bossy saith, "Oh yeah - I forgot! You got me there, Pete!"

Now it was the first Day of the *Festival of Di* and his groupies came unto him, and said, "Where wilt thou that we should book for our *Di Day* dinner?"

And he saith, "Do ye get on the phone and give unto Jason who runneth the Wholefood Emporium a bell. Enquire of him whether he can slot us in. Except it be not too late, for ye know I have a big day on the morrow."

But Phil saith, "Facilitator, let it not be the wholefood place, I beseech thee. For lo, the abundance of lentils is too great, and we fart, so that men do hold their noses and speak not with us. And it doeth naught for us with the totty likewise."

And Matty saith also, "Man shall not live by carrot juice alone, neither by green things which be the coney food."

And Sim saith, "Say no more the wholefood place that is Jason's. Say rather that Chinky behind Smithfield."

But Jon crieth in a loud voice, "Let it not be that Chinky behind Smithfield - for verily aforetimes it giveth me Livingstone's Revenge, and that mightily."

And some said, "This place, Facilitator!" and others,

"No, let it rather be that!" Save every one of them was of one mind that it might not be the carrot juice again.

But he put them all to silence and saith, "For this cause have I chosen to drink the carrot juice with you and eat the lentils: for that the People fill the great City on Di Day and, behold, they be very careful to watch the Facilitator to see what he will eat and what he will drink. And I must be an example to them, that they henceforth eat healthily."

When he heard these word, Pete was much discomfited and he saith, "Aw go on, just this once - the Smithfield Chinky!"

But he answered, "No. It is not for you to say 'Lo, let us go to the Chinky' or 'Behold, we haven't been for a curry for generations.' But that all might be fulfilled which is written of the Facilitator that in all things he doth live the healthy lifestyle."

And their hearts groaned within them. But Matty saith, "Nevertheless, Facilitator, let it be as thou dost desire."

"THAT'S MY NEWSPAPER ARTICLE ON THE IMPORTANCE OF A PURE AND SIMPLE LIFE FINISHED PASS THE CHAMPERS, MAGDA LOVE"

And when the hour was come, they departed that place and came unto Jason's restaurant, even to the place of the wholefood and the carrot juice which is exceeding carroty and the lentils, behold, the which are full of farts. Now when the Festival of Di was fully come he did sit down with his groupies. And as he did eat, he saith, "Verily I say unto you, one of you will shop me to the old farts."

But, hearing these things, Pete saith unto him, "Dunno about old farts, Facilitator: there's plenty of new farts in these 'ere lentils!"

But he rebuked him, saying, "Make no mockery, neither jesting which is not convenient."

But Pete saith unto him, "Aw c'mon it was only a joke!"

And Bossy looked on Pete and, lo, he was exceeding sorrowful and saith unto him, "The days shall come, yea they are with us already, when there shall be no more jesting nor sayings that are not convenient. For lo, there shall be a new commandment which saith, 'Thou shalt not say anything which it happeneth might be offensive unto them that are obese or aesthetically-challenged or partially-sighted or hearing-impaired or differently-abled. Neither unto them that are of the foreign religions that are all peace and love unto men nor even unto them that do fart a lot.'"

But Jim the son of Zeb questioned him saying "But the foreign religions be not all peace and love. Behold was not my cousin Sharon of the fishnet tights on that bus what was blown up down Tavistock Square that time. That was done by the fanatics of the religion that ye mention."

"Verily," saith Andy, "but she is still a babe for that she has but three fingers on her left hand."

"And my old grandad marcheth into Aden with

Mad Mitch. One of his mates were killed by one of those that followeth this religion of peace and love. Mind you, Mad Mitch giveth them all a damn good kicking to teacheth them a lesson. Blessed be the name of Mad Mitch."

So Bossy grew wroth and rebuketh them saying "Have ye learned nothing? Have I not said unto you that the Truth is greater than the facts. What you tell me are mere facts. But I tell thee the Truth."

And concerning him that should shop him unto the old farts, they all began to say, "Is it I, Facilitator?"

And he saith, "He that giveth me the second helping of farty lentils, it is he that shall shop me to the old farts!"

And he began to be much pleased and very jolly and his groupies were glad, even very glad, so that Andy saith, "Sod me - I didn't know you could have such fun on carrot juice!"

And, as they were eating, Bossy took the bowl of lentils and, making a New Age sign over it, ladleth it out unto the groupies and saith, "Whenever ye eat of the lentils, remember what exceeding good the fibre doeth for the prevention of the irritable bowel syndrome." And he took the juicer and saith, "Remember thy carrot juice which is filled with carotene and that helpeth thee see in the dark. For I say unto you that I shall no more eat of the wholefood nor drink of the juices that come forth from the juicer until I eat and drink with you afresh when the Great Modernisation is come."

And when they had sung that old ballad by Queen, behold, they went unto the Mount that is called Primrose, and he saith, "All of ye shall be offended because of me this night. And lo, the Son of the Latest Thing shall be delivered into the hands of them that are politically-incorrect, and they shall mock him and satirise him. But after I make my comeback I will go with you unto Romford, and Southend and unto the uttermost parts of Essex."

And they departed that place and went unto Kew Gardens. And when he had drawn apart from his groupies he began to be rather pissed off. And he remembereth his mantra which had been given unto him by the Guru. And he began to say within himself,

"Don't be pissed off, just go with the flow;

You're the Son of the Latest Thing, you know!"

And while he yet spake, behold, he that should betray him, even his groupie Jude the Obscure, drew nigh and kissed him.

And Bossy saith, "Ooh, you are bold!"

Jude the Obscure replieth. "Great news, Guru. I just downloaded an email from thine account. The producers of the show that declareth itself the Factor of X hath decreed that there will be a special show on the morrow in which thee shall proclaim thy message of political correctness unto the world. And thou wilt be interviewed by Poppy Pilates (which was called for his exceeding craftiness in the weird exercises) who hath been instructed to ask what are known as the soft questions. And thou shalt be broadcast unto the nations.

So Bossy saith "Thus it is written that the Moderniser shall modernise the world. Let us go down unto the studios to prepare for the broadcast." Then did Bossy call unto him Matt the groupie who did write the Blog for the righteous and did say "Matt get thyself blogging double quick. I'm going to be on the Factor of X tomorrow evening and I want the entire audience packed with our PC supporters, yea so that the crowd do cheer and chant as I prolcaimeth the Modernisation." And behold Matt did the blogging, and the righteous did retweet the blog and did leave their homes to gather unto the Factor of X.

And Jude the Obscure did smile most secretly, and did text Hack who did text Fogey. And there was great rejoicing amongst those Kippers who knew what was to come.

And it came to pass that next evening Bossy came unto the great dome wherein the Factor of X was to be filmed. And when the *Festival of Di* was fully come, they were all with one accord in the great dome.

And Bossy stood before the host, whose name was Poppy Pilates, which saith unto him, "Art thou the Son of the Latest Thing, the Moderniser General?"

"Yea, verily" replied Bossy. "Give me the mike Grandad and be amazed at my coolness." Then did Bossy speak unto the cameras, and yet unto the audience that was delivered unto him by the blogging of Matt and the tweeting of the righteous. And Bossy did speak of the evils of racism and they did cheer. And he did speak of the goodness of multiculturalism and they did cheer. He spoke of the climate change that was because of the wickedness of human kind and they did cheer. And he spoke of the need to despoil the countryside with wind turbines and for all the righteous to drive hybrid cars and they did cheer. And he did proclaim that the Truth is greater than the facts. He did speak of all manner of Political Correctness and with every clause and admonition the audience of the great and the good did cheer. Then did Bossy give up the mike for he was lauded by the audience.

Then did the second contestant in the Factor that was X step on the stage. And behold it was Fogey with Hack as his companion. And they did put on a presentation that was wondrous in its Political Incorrectness. Fogey did show the climate graphs that did demonstrate that climate change was natural and normal and nothing to be afraid of. Fogey did put forth data showing that renewable power sources were inefficient, expensive and moreover were unreliable so that the nation would be plunged into darkness one cold winter's night. Fogey showed that multiculturalism did breed ghettos wherein the poor remained poor and the bigotted remained bigotted, much to the benefit of the politicians for whom they voted, whereas integration did free the bigotted to see the bigger picture and to thrive. Fogey did demonstrate how comprehensive schools did provide a deficient education and so did trap the poor in poverty, while grammar schools did give them a solid education and so liberated them to better themselves and their fellows. Then he did play the music of Bach and of Mozart and did demonstrate its subtlety and its beauty. All manner of Political Incorrectness did Fogey proclaim. And the audience, that which Matt the groupie had summoned by means of the www, did boo him and heckled him but he regardeth them not.

And then did Hack step forward. He did show forth his photos of Bossy and Magda swigging the champers by the pool at their millionaires pad in the hills outside Romford. He did explain the paper trail of the vast profits that did accrue from the Centre for Political Correctness in Romford, even that which is staffed by young ladies of obvious charms, and how they were moved to an offshore account kept by Sebastian the Agent, from whence it went to tax free territories wherein the accounts were held by Bossy and by Magda.

And then did Hack demonstrate how some of the money was invested into companies that did clear fell the rainforests for vast profits, did employ child labour in sweat shops for higher cash returns and did manufacture cigarettes and oil and coal and fur coats and all manner of other Politically Incorrect goods for the cash profit of Bossy and of Magda and of Sebastian the Agent.

And the audience did fall silent for the prophet was unmasked. And when Bossy saw he was accused of Fogey and Hack, he answered them nothing.

Then said Poppy Pilates unto him, "Answerest thou nothing? Behold, thou hast despised the jackpot with the which our sponsors do sponsor our Quiz withal, and yet Hack here does reveal thee to be as greedy as the next bastard with his snout in the trough. Thou canst not hope to gain the prize if thou answerest nothing."

But he answered to him never a word, so that present marvelled, and said, "Phew, what a showstopper! Well, folks, I guess there's always a first time for everything!"

And being accustomed to, like, humourless abasements, the multitude did fall about, and say, "He hath of a surety more mirth than that which is called Ben Elton." And so spake they all.

And then did Poppy Pilates call upon the audience to vote for the winner by pressing their buttons. And they do press them. And the whirling graphics revealed that they had selected Bossy. And then did Poppy Pilates declare unto the cameras. "Now folks that is just our audience here. The true vote lieth with you out there. With you, the great British public. Do you vote for Bossy of Islington with his Political Correctness or with Fogey with his Freedom. And Bossy smiled for the audience was with him and the spirit of Political Correctness was over the land.

And the whirling graphics did whirl again. And they revealed that they had selected Fogey. For behold, the people of the country preferred Freedom and had not been led astray by the prophet that was but a wolf in sheep's clothing.

Then saith Pilates unto Fogey, "And what shall we do, then, with this Bossy which is called 'Facilitator' and 'Moderniser General'?"

And he did cry out, "Let him be satirised." But Poppy Pilates said, "Why? He's a regular kinda guy."

But Fogey did speak unto the camera and did summon the People to twitter and facebook and lo, the www was filled with the cry "Let him be satirised!" for the people had spoken. And Fogey did say "Thus let it be written. 'He who liveth by the www shall die by the www'."

And when Poppy Pilates saw that he could do nothing except that which the pole had voted and the whirling graphics had shown to be verily the desire of the People, he did put forward Fogey for the jackpot, and Bossy he delivered unto them to be satirised. And Poppy did say "Stuff me, last time I let the public have a free vote."

In which BOSSY DEPARTETH

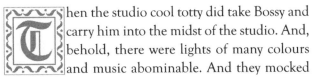hen the studio cool totty did take Bossy and carry him into the midst of the studio. And, behold, there were lights of many colours and music abominable. And they mocked him there, saying, "We had thought that thou shouldst be the one which bringeth in the General Modernisation, but, behold, thou hast been knocked out in the preliminary round, as it is written, 'By the select button shall he be deselected.'"

And they put the yellow wellies on him and do bring forth the Booby Bonnet and lay it upon his head. And they do pour over him the paint of many colours. And the canned laughter mocked him also.

And all his groupies departed, like unto the sheep, sheepishly, and left him alone - except for the studio audience and fifteen million viewers nationwide. After that they had taken the piss out of him, they took from off his head and led him away to be satirised. And when they were come unto a game show that is called *Gollygosh*! They satirised him there. And they did set up the studio banner and the superscription of his accusation: THIS IS Bossy THE MODERNISER GENERAL.

And, behold, Fogey which stood where he was satirised said also, "He modernised others. Himself he cannot modernise!" Then were two stand-up comedians of the Politically-Correct kind also satirised with him - the one on his right hand and the other on his left. And one also took the piss, saying, "Thou that would make the People Politically-Correct, give us a presentation on compliance now!"

But the other which was satirised with him said, "Let him be. For we are justly satirised for that we weren't very funny. But this guy, behold, he hath had a fantastic run."

And after three hours of this, the studio lights did fail and all the People went "Ooh!" And when the engineers couldn't get the sodding lights to come on again, behold, all the People went off home.

Then Bossy, knowing that he'd had a great run and

that even the best contestants get deselected eventually (for the People do weary of them all and look for all things to be made new) did laugh and cry out, "OK, Latest Thing - bring it on, then!"

And when he had thus said, he departed unto the green room. And, behold, the cool totty did give him the full body massage and the reflexology with that which is called "camomile tea".

And when they saw that he had dozed off, they left him lying there. Then cometh Mad Magda, early, while *Breakfast TV* had not yet started, unto the studio. And she seeth two guys in white apparel cleaning the loo and they say unto her, "He's not here, lady - he's gone for an audition." And Magda stood in the foyer twiddling her thumbs. And, behold, she was freaked out. And when she had turned back, she saw Bossy and knew not that it was he.

And Bossy saith unto her, "Baby, why art thou freaked out and, like, wasted?"

But she, supposing him to be the Commissionaire, saith, "They've taken our kid off for an audition and I know not which bloody studio he's gone to."

And Bossy saith unto her, "Magda!"

And she saith unto him, "My Facilitator and my Moderniser General!" Which, being interpreted is, "The Latest Thing on the Earth". But he saith unto her, "Don't touch me. For, behold, after that they had given me the camomile tea, the cool totty cracked a few bottles and we got rather a lot down our necks. I've got this kingsized hangover and exceeding crapulence, so that, like, you wouldn't believe. Anyway, I've got my comeback in three days. I'll call Percy of the Beeb who will setteth it up for us."

And, behold, she smileth and saith "Listen, clever socks, the party's over. The gig don't jive no more. It's time to get out. Now listen. Sebastian is flogging everything he can and moving the cash offshore, but we have to move fast as that damn Hack hath given his files unto the tax inspector and they are hot on our trail. We've got to get to Jersey fast to sign some forms, then

on to the Bahamas to sign some more. If we don't shift fast we'll lose the lot. Sebastian is doing what he can, but he needs our signatures. So stuff your bloody hangover and come with me."

And Bossy did see that she spake wisely and went with her.

Then in the Street that is Downing did the new Prime Bureaucrat who is Right On meet with Helen of the Opposition and with Percy of the Beeb and with such others of the great and the good that were righteous in the eyes of the Politically Correct. And the Prime Bureaucrat did say "What the hell are we going to do now? The people have kicked out Bossy and we're going to be next. They've tumbled this PC palaver is a pile of dingo's kidneys."

And the others did look at him askance for the word 'palaver' was most Politically Incorrect being based on a colonialist view of the downtrodden native peoples of colour.

"Well," saith Helen of the Opposition. "The first thing is we must never allow the People to have a vote ever again, unless it be to choose who will sing in a West End Show or some other unimportant drivel. Certainly we won't have a referendum on the blessed EU or some such. The People might vote the wrong way, the uneducated chavs."

"But the election," quoth Percy of the Beeb. "You cannot scrap the General Election and it is due in three months."

"Verily," smileth Helen. "But the election is between me and the new Prime Bureaucrat who is Right On. And we are both fully signed up to the Political Correctness. So whichever way the People vote we can keep Political Correctness in power. And you, Percy, will keep it dominating the air waves. We can bump you up to being the boss of Ofcom so you can get that Fogey sacked for a start. And the flow of government funds to Politically Correct groups and projects and individuals will continue to flow, no matter what the People want. They don't know what is good for them, but luckily we do."

"Yea," quoth Percy of the Beeb. "And we deserve top salaries and stonking great expense accounts for that we are wise in the ways of Political Correctness and know what is good for the ignorant chavs even though they don't."

"Damn right," saith the Prime Bureaucrat who is Right On. "I'll set up a new Office of Righteousness, the boss of which will have a vast salary and the stonkingest expense account. Then whoever shall winneth the General Election, the other leader may be the boss of OffRight." And so it came to pass.

And in Romford did Simmy, which is called Pete; Andy his brother; Jim the son of Zeb; and Jon (not the Aquatherapist); Phil, Bart, Tom and Matty the VAT man; Jim the son of Alf (which in the days of their political-incorrectness was called "the cripple") continue to attend unto the Center for Political Correctness, even that which is staffed by young ladies of obvious charms.

For it was mandated by Percy of the Beeb that none could work in television or radio unless they had undertaken courses in multiculturalism and in climate change awareness and in other such shibboleths of the righteous. And lo! Those that did not learn the buzzwords and believe the doctrines did not get jobs. And Helen of the Opposition, who did become the new Prime Bureaucrat after the election did mandate that nobody could work in the public sector unless they too undertook the courses and believed the doctrines. And so it came to pass that all the great and the good, those that did guzzle the troughs of public funds, did become Politically Correct and did oppress those who were not Politically Correct and did all the real work.

In which BOSSY comes again

And it came to pass some years later that Phil and Andy were walking up unto Emmaus, the restaurant of the fine tofu that standeth close unto Mansion House tube station, for lo it was suppertime. And as they sat at table the waitress brought them bread. And Andy saith "Get a load of that babe. I wouldn't mind giving her a job down the Centre in Romford."

But Phil saith, "Mind not the totty. Look over there." And he did point towards a gleaming Bentley that was parked over the other side of the road, close unto a bank. And emerging from the car was a man wondrously dressed in the sharpest of sharp suits, hand-tailored withal. And with him was a woman dripping with gold and diamonds. "Verily, does not that posh bloke look a bit like Bossy?"

"Indeed," quoth Andy. "And the posh totty is not unlike Magda. I always did fancy her."

"But it can't be," saith Phil, "for did not Bossy tell us that he was ascending up to the Himalayas for a rest cure at some right-on monastery of poverty and chastity."

"And did not Magda say she was off to look after her sick old mum up north," responded Andy. And they fell to eating their tofu and organic ciabatta and other righteous food.

And over the way, close unto the Bentley, Magda did say "I don't like being here, someone might recognise us."

"Worry ye not," replieth Bossy. "For who is here that would recognise us dressed like this. Anyway, we've got to clear out the safety deposit box that is here that Sebastian did stuff with the kruger rands and blood diamonds, then we can scarper back to the Bahamas and live the life of Reilly for ever. And we need the dosh if we are to send little Bossy to Eton and little Magda to Roedean. Those posh

places aren't cheap you know." And they passed on into the bank.

Then did the chauffeur in the Rolls Royce turn on the radio and hear the voices of the righteous sounding through the airwaves. For lo it was Percy of the Beeb delivering the annual Reith Lectures, and as he finished he did proclaim "And go ye into the Great City and unto the uttermost parts of the European Superstate, preaching and teaching them Compliance, Standard Practice, Social Inclusion and Equal Opportunities for all, regardless of age, race, gender or disability.

"And lo, Political-Correctness is with you always, even unto the end of the world."

"The End"

Hilarious definitions of words and phrases used in today's world that are guaranteed to amuse, annoy, appeal and appal in equal measure.

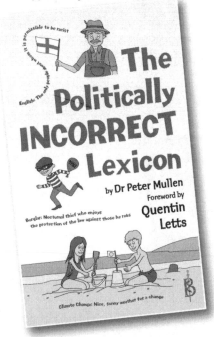

Today's media and politics are dominated by words and phrases that have a special meaning far removed from their traditional dictionary definitions. In this hugely entertaining lexicon, Peter Mullen exposes the hidden meanings, secret definitions and doublespeak of the modern English language as used by the politically correct. Examples include:

Human Rights: A legal fiction designed to make rich lawyers even richer
English: The only people about whom it is permissible to be racist.
Burglar: Nocturnal thief who enjoys the protection of the law against those he robs.
Climate Change: Nice, sunny weather for a change
Reforms: Destruction. As in "educational reforms".

Partner: A sexual partner of more than three nights duration.
Celebrity: Someone you've never heard of
Friend: The associate of a celebrity who sells details of the celeb's private life to the tabloids

About the Author

The Reverend Peter Mullen is religious columnist for the Daily Mail, and has recently retired as Rector of St Michael's Cornhill - one of Sir Christopher Wren's churches in the City of London. He is also Chaplain to the Stock Exchange and Chaplain to the Guild of Air Pilots. Peter writes a regular column in the Wall Street Journal and occasionally for the Daily Telegraph. He has been a vicar in the Church of England since 1970, officiating at parishes in Yorkshire before moving to London.